Workbook

Gateway

2nd Edition

Lynda Edwards
Patricia Reilly

macmillan education

B2+

Contents B2+

1 Interact!

Reading

1a VOCABULARY Find eight parts of the body in the word search.

Y	Q	T	B	N	E	C	K	N	K	A	S
D	V	H	A	Y	L	E	T	Y	H	B	J
B	E	U	C	V	Y	S	B	G	A	P	C
I	X	M	K	E	E	O	E	A	N	M	E
W	O	B	D	H	M	L	T	W	D	D	P
V	P	G	C	X	J	M	H	U	U	Y	R
N	A	S	H	O	U	L	D	E	R	H	X
W	U	Q	O	K	L	C	U	I	F	C	I

1b Which five body parts from 1 are used in idioms for these definitions?

1 agree with someone ......eye......
2 tease someone ....
3 help someone ....
4 be totally influenced by someone ....
5 ignore someone ....

1c Choose the correct answers.

1 They're joking about it – they're .... your leg.
A turning B pushing C pulling

2 I never agree with Henry about anything. We just don't .... eye-to-eye.
A see B look C watch

3 Katy won't speak to me. Why is she giving me the .... shoulder?
A stiff B cold C hard

4 I hate it when people do things behind my .... without me knowing.
A shoulder B chest C back

5 Jenny does everything her brother tells her to do. She's completely under his ....
A eye B thumb C hand

6 I need some help. Can you .... me a hand?
A lend B put C take

7 Jaden took a risk to help Sara. He stuck his .... out for her.
A neck B thumb C leg

8 I was really worried about changing schools, but I talked to my mum about it. It was great to get that off my ....
A back B chest C shoulders

2 Look at the article headlines and photos. Do you think the statements are True (T) or False (F)?

1 There have been Free Hugs campaigns in different countries. T/F
2 Individuals in a crowd don't always help in emergencies because they don't want to be different from other people. T/F
3 The photos in the Humans of New York project are not accompanied by any information. T/F
4 Talking to someone you don't know has no influence on your mood. T/F

3 Read the articles quickly and check your guesses.

4 Read the articles again. For questions 1–8 choose from the four texts (A–D). The texts may be chosen more than once.

Which text describes a project, experiment or research that …

- proved that groups have an effect on individual behaviour? 1 ....
- proves our assumptions about interacting with people we don't know are incorrect? 2 ....
- had the same result for different personality types? 3 ....
- shows that strangers can benefit from physical contact? 4 ....
- required people to share information about their lives? 5 ....
- describes a way of getting assistance in a difficult situation? 6 ....
- involved participants setting up their own projects? 7 ....
- showed that people really enjoy learning about other humans' experiences? 8 ....

5 CRITICAL THINKING

To what extent do you think these projects and experiments are important for society? What could be done in schools to improve the way people interact?

6 Match the underlined words and phrases in the articles with the definitions.

1 not willing to do something ....
2 complete, including many details ....
3 when you see something for a moment ....
4 not supported with facts or evidence ....
5 very interesting, especially because of being mysterious or strange ....
6 starting a conversation, especially with someone you do not know ....
7 stopped doing something because a lot of people opposed it ....

A

FREE HUGS ARE TAKING OVER THE WORLD

A hug from a stranger can change your life – or at least it did for Juan Mann.

He had been living in London when he suddenly had to move back to his hometown of Sydney, Australia. But he felt like a tourist; he had no one to welcome him and no home to go to. Despite going out and talking to people, he found making friends hard because too many people seemed more interested in their mobile phones and the Internet than talking to him.

So one day, he took matters into his own hands. He made a giant sign and stood holding it in the busiest shopping area in the city. The sign said 'Free Hugs' on both sides. He only had to wait for 15 minutes before he got his first hug from an elderly lady. She explained that her dog had just died and the hug had made her feel better. Soon Mann was hugging all sorts of strangers every few seconds. Everyone seemed to feel better after hugging him and he returned day after day. Other people came with their own signs and joined him. The police tried to ban the movement, but over 10,000 people signed a petition supporting Mann and they backed down.

When Mann posted a video on YouTube of his story, he thought a few people might watch it. He had no idea his campaign was about to go viral. The video attracted over 70 million views and massive worldwide interest. Mann set up his website to help people start their own Free Hugs campaigns and since then, thousands of people have taken part in many different countries including India, Switzerland, Portugal and the UK.

C

HUMANS OF NEW YORK
Photos with a story

Most of us are fascinated by other people's lives. We like to know who they are and where they're from, and this was the inspiration for Brandon Stanton when he started the Humans of New York (HONY) project.

His dream initially was to create a comprehensive record of the city's inhabitants by taking people's photos and marking them on a map to show where he had photographed them. He started the project in 2010. After several months, he realised his project was turning into something more intriguing. Stanton had started chatting to the people he photographed. They told him an astonishing variety of things, from their plans for the day to their deepest secrets. He published these short stories and quotes along with the portraits and his photoblog Humans of New York was born.

Now HONY has over eight million followers worldwide on social media. People love the daily glimpses into the lives of strangers. Each person remains anonymous, but shares a special piece of their own unique history. The photos are remarkably varied and every HONY blogpost gets many comments, with people sharing their own stories, giving advice or simply admiring Stanton's work.

Anyone in New York could be a HONY subject.

B

WHY YOU DON'T WANT TO HAVE AN EMERGENCY IN A CROWD

If you witnessed an emergency right in front of you, would you try to help? We might like to think so but psychologists believe that this is not always the case.

They believe that whether we help or not depends on the number of people around us and that the greater number of people present, the less likely we are to help. Psychologists have been studying this behaviour since 1964, when a group of bystanders observing a serious crime did nothing, not even call the police.

This phenomenon is called the 'Bystander Effect' because in an emergency the presence of other people actually discourages an individual from taking action. Why? Firstly, when there is a group of people, no one person feels responsible. Everyone thinks someone else will take charge, especially if they are in a hurry. Secondly, people are reluctant to stand out from the crowd; if someone sees others failing to react to a situation, they see this as a sign that it isn't necessary to take action themselves. Nobody wants to be seen to be doing something different from others and so nobody does anything.

In contrast, when there are only one or two people, there is no pressure to behave like everyone else and nobody else to take responsibility, so people are much more likely to act. So how do you prevent the bystander effect if you are in trouble? Psychologists recommend making eye contact with someone in the crowd, asking that person specifically for help. By personalising your request, it becomes much harder to turn you down.

D

TALKING TO STRANGERS MAKES US HAPPIER

What do you do when you travel on public transport by yourself? Do you get out your phone or do you talk to other passengers? Most people's fear of interacting with strangers means they sit silently on their journeys, but new research has shown that they might be happier if they didn't.

Researchers in Chicago have conducted an experiment with train commuters, with some participants asked to start a conversation with a stranger and others told not to talk. The participants who had talked to a stranger later rated their journey as most positive while those who had kept silent reported the most negative experience. Interestingly, participants' worst fear – being rejected by the stranger – proved totally unfounded as strangers were happy to engage in conversation and nobody was rejected. Even more surprisingly, the results were the same for both introverts and extroverts; both personality types were able to have a conversation.

In another experiment, participants talked to strangers in a waiting room. The participants and the people they talked to all reported feeling happier after chatting, and they also noted that the waiting time had passed more quickly.

These results show that we don't talk because we think breaking the ice is going to be awkward and people won't want to talk to us. In reality, however, there's nothing to fear and the conversations can have a positive effect on our lives.

1 Write the verbs in bold next to the correct tense (a–g).

1 Mann **had been living** in London and he didn't know anyone there.
2 After several months, he realised his project **was turning** into something more intriguing.
3 He had no idea his campaign **was about to go** viral.
4 Psychologists **have been studying** this behaviour since 1964.
5 He **started** the project in 2010.
6 Research **has shown** that talking to strangers makes us happier.
7 The participants who **had talked** to a stranger rated their journey as most positive.

a past simple ....
b past continuous ....
c present perfect simple ....
d present perfect continuous ....
e past perfect ....
f past perfect continuous ....
g future in the past ....

2 Circle the correct alternative.

1 I didn't know the girl's name because I <u>had forgotten/had been forgetting</u> it.
2 Psychologists <u>have done/have been doing</u> experiments on human behaviour for many years.
3 When I arrived, Lucy and Steve were already there. They <u>chatted/were chatting</u> about the party.
4 Tom had a red face because he <u>had run/had been running</u>.
5 I got up late so I <u>missed/was missing</u> my train.

3 Choose the correct answers.

1 Sam .... what his brother tells him to do.
A always did B has always done
C had always done
2 We thought the boys ...., but luckily in the end they didn't.
A have argued B were about to argue
C had been arguing
3 We went to Italy last month. We .... there many times.
A went B were going C have been
4 Mark .... his homework when I phoned, so he could chat.
A has just finished B had just finished
C had just been finishing
5 Simon .... in Portugal before he moved to Asia.
A had been living B has been living
C has lived

4 Complete the dialogue with the correct form of the verbs given. Sometimes more than one form is possible.

A: So I hear that Jenna **(a)** .... (finally/decide) to study psychology at university. I really thought that she **(b)** .... (choose) sociology.

B: I know. She **(c)** .... (hesitate) between the two for a while now. Apparently she **(d)** .... (change) her mind after she **(e)** .... (go) to a talk by Professor Martin last week.

A: Oh yes, I wanted to go to that, but I **(f)** .... (already/arrange) to go to an Ed Sheeran gig with Katie. We **(g)** .... (look forward) to it for ages so there was no way I **(h)** .... (cancel)!

B: I don't blame you. I **(i)** .... (think) about going too, but they **(j)** .... (sell out). I went to the lecture instead.

A: Right! So was he a good lecturer?

B: Fantastic. But they **(k)** .... (have) a few technical problems during the talk. He **(l)** .... (show) some photos of an experiment he **(m)** .... (carry out) in the US when there was a power cut and everything went dark.

A: So what happened?

B: He's such a professional. While they **(n)** .... (fix) the problem, he talked in the dark! It was fascinating, he really **(o)** .... (make) me want to study psychology.

A: It sounds good, but the gig was absolutely brilliant. I don't think you need to be a psychologist to explain why my evening was better than yours!

GRAMMAR CHALLENGE

5 Complete the sentences using the words given. Do not change the meaning.

1 I like comics. I started liking them when I was a child. **since**
I *have liked comics since* I was a child.
2 The film started before we got to the cinema. **already**
The film .... when we got to the cinema.
3 Jane started running 30 minutes ago and she is still running. **for**
Jane .... 30 minutes.
4 Jack was studying for hours, then he had lunch. **been**
Jack .... before having lunch.
5 We were playing football in the park when Kate broke her arm. **while**
Kate .... in the park.
6 They were going to go home. **about**
They .... home.

1 Complete the table with the noun form of these words.

accurate • argue • describe • frequent
happy • interact • invent • lonely • move
personal • psychology • research • science
similar • sincere • speak

-ion	………, ………, ………
-ity	………, ………, ………
-er	………, ………
-cy	………, ………
-ness	………, ………
-ist	………, ………
-ment	………, ………

2 Complete the sentences with the correct form of the words given.

1 ……… (accurate) is important in scientific research.
2 ……… (friend) is a close relationship between two people who are friends.
3 ……… (fail) isn't always a bad thing. It can be positive when you learn from it.
4 It's important to have the ……… (free) to do what you want in life.
5 ……… (safe) at work and school is important.
6 We have so much technology that we interact less with people. That is why many people are ……… (loneliness).

3 Complete the text with the correct form of the words given.

'Thank you' is one of the first **(a)** ……… we learn to say and it is considered an important sign of good manners. However, apart from being an **(b)** ……… of gratitude, saying thank you can also be beneficial in many ways. **(c)** ……… have carried out studies into how being grateful affects us. These involved asking **(d)** ……… to send job applications to various different people and request feedback. The people who were thanked for their help were more willing to help a second time because they felt it was a more enjoyable **(e)** ……… . While this was not particularly surprising, the **(f)** ……… who carried out the experiments also found that people were more willing to help a stranger as a result. It is apparent that when we are thanked we feel valued and have more **(g)** ……… . Being thanked increases our **(h)** ……… and because we feel more positive this gives us the **(i)** ……… to agree to help strangers when asked.

EXPRESS
INDICATE
PSYCHOLOGY
PARTICIPATE
INTERACT
RESEARCH
CONFIDE
HAPPY
MOTIVATE

4 LISTENING 01 Listen to an interview and choose the best summary.

1 It's about why you should join social networking sites.
2 It's about different speciality sites.
3 It's about sites for people with annoying habits.

5 01 Listen again. Are the statements True (T), False (F), or is the information Not Mentioned (NM)?

1 Pinterest had millions of followers as soon as it started. T/F/NM
2 Pinterest is now the third largest social networking site in the world. T/F/NM
3 As a member of Trot On, you can share photos and videos and join speciality groups. T/F/NM
4 Dogster has far more members than Catster. T/F/NM
5 There are over a million users on the site REMcloud where people can share their dreams. T/F/NM
6 It is free to use RedKaraoke to sing with people all over the world. T/F/NM

VOCABULARY EXTENSION

6 Complete the table with the adjective form of these verbs and nouns.

appear • confide • depend • ~~ignore~~ • innocence
insist • obey • please • resist • to erate • vibrate

-ant	*ignorant*	………	………
	………	………	
-ent	………	………	………
	………	………	………

1 Match the uses (1–6) with the examples (a–f).

a It **used to be** a small website.
b I **would go** riding in the summer holidays.
c They**'ll** share knitting patterns with fellow enthusiasts.
d I **was always** posting ideas.
e I **never remember** my dreams.
f My dog **is always behaving** badly.

1 *will* for present habits ......
2 present simple for present habits ......
3 *used to* for past habits and states ......
4 *would* for past habits ......
5 present continuous for present habits ......
6 past continuous for past habits ......

2 Are the sentences about a present (PR) or past (PA) habit?

1 Mum **will interrupt** me every time I explain something to her. ......
2 Dad **would leave** the house at 6.30 every morning and take the 6.50 train to London. ......
3 At weekends Fran **will do** the cooking and I'll do the washing-up. ......
4 My sister **is always borrowing** my MP3 player. ......
5 I **usually stay on** at school to do an extra maths class on Thursdays. ......
6 I **used to have** a tiny portable TV in my bedroom when I was eleven. ......
7 When we were younger, my sister **was always playing** her music loudly. ......
8 Sam **would arrive** late for school every day so the teachers gave him extra homework. ......

3 Circle the correct alternative.

1 When she was a teenager my sister *will wear/used to wear* lots of make-up.
2 Our last English teacher *would never let/was never letting* us watch DVDs in class.
3 My parents *would always ask/are always asking* me to babysit. It's not fair!
4 I *was attending/used to attend* a computer club on Saturday mornings.
5 My brother Peter *will knock/would knock* on my door and wake me up when he comes home late.
6 When he was a child, Mark *was always getting/will get* into trouble.
7 I *used to get/will usually get* up late at the weekend if I'm not busy.
8 We *often go/are often going* to the beach in the summer.

4 Complete the sentences with one appropriate word.

1 Katie and Rob .... always complaining. Why can't they be more positive?
2 When they were very young, they .... pull the dog's tail. It didn't like it at all.
3 I like Ruth, but she .... tell you other people's secrets. It's a habit of hers I can't stand.
4 We were always .... games in the woods when I was a child.
5 My dad .... always watch football on a Saturday when there was usually a good film on.
6 I think people are generally good. They .... always do the right thing.
7 Simon .... often forget important things, so I was surprised when he forgot Sue's birthday.

5 Rewrite the sentences using the words given. Do not change the meaning.

1 Lisa often argues with her sister, it's terrible. **always**
Lisa ....
2 I walked to school every day when I was a child. **used**
I ....
3 Ben played games all the time last summer. **would**
Ben ....
4 They usually go to the cinema on Sunday evening if they aren't busy. **will**
They ....
5 He played tennis for hours every day. **was**
He ....

GRAMMAR CHALLENGE

6 Choose the correct answers.

1 When my dad .... in town, he gave me a lift to college every morning.
A would work B has worked C used to work
2 When we were younger, my sister .... my clothes without asking. It drove me crazy!
A will borrow B was always borrowing
C had been borrowing
3 When Joe was learning to drive, he .... an accident.
A used to have B would have C had
4 We .... to Scotland on holiday every summer when I was a child, which I loved.
A would go B have been going
C were always going
5 Last year, our teacher .... us use dictionaries in exams. I suppose that was fair.
A was never letting B would never let
C will never let
6 I started playing basketball when I was eight, and I .... it ever since.
A have been playing B was playing C am playing

1 LISTENING 02 **Listen to part of a personal interview between an examiner and a candidate. Put the questions in the correct order.**

a What's the best way to learn a language? ....
b What do you usually do on holiday? ....
c What do you like doing in your free time? ....
d Who has been the most important person in your life so far? ....

2 02 **Listen again. Are the sentences True (T) or False (F)?**

1 Tomas gives more than one piece of information in each answer. T / F
2 He doesn't use a variety of tenses. T / F
3 He uses two different expressions to play for time. T / F
4 He doesn't use any expressions to express opinions. T / F
5 He uses an expression to add examples. T / F

3 02 **Complete the table with these expressions. Then tick (✓) the ones Tomas uses. Listen again if necessary.**

As far as I'm concerned • For example
For instance • Hmm • In fact • I think
Let me think about that for a second • Personally
The thing is • To my mind • Well

Playing for time	
Adding examples and ideas	
Expressing opinions	

4 **Read these extracts from a personal interview between an interviewer (I) and candidate (C) and complete them with an appropriate phrase from 3. Use a different phrase from each section for each extract.**

1

I: What have you found most interesting about studying English?

C: **(a)** ...., it's probably all the cultural information you learn as you study. **(b)** .... we read a lot about music festivals in England. That's really cool. **(c)** .... when you learn a language you should really try to go on holiday to the country to practise and find out more about the culture.

2

I: What do you usually do at the weekend?

C: **(d)** .... on Saturday, I usually meet my friends and we do different things. **(e)** .... we go shopping or we go to the cinema or we go for a pizza. I'll usually spend Sunday with my parents, brother and cousins. **(f)** .... it's important to spend time with your family.

3

I: How did you spend your last holiday?

C: I went to England. I've been visiting the same family in London every summer since I was 11 years old! **(g)** .... it's a great way to practise my English! What do we usually do? **(h)** ...., we do lots of different things. **(i)** .... we visit famous museums and monuments, we go to restaurants and we do sports.

5 **Now write your answers to the three questions in 4.**

....
....
....

6 **Choose two more of the personal questions below. Think about what you would include in each answer. Write a paragraph for each answer. Remember to include expressions from 3 and a variety of tenses in your answers.**

- Which electronic gadget is most important to you? Why?
- If you could choose, where would you spend your next holiday?
- How important is sport in your life?
- Do you usually study alone or with other people? Why?
- What qualities are important in a friend?
- Why do you think it is important to learn languages?

1 Complete the similes below.

1 as light as ....
2 as easy as ....
3 as strong as ....
4 as clear as ....
5 as quick as ....
6 as solid as ....
7 as cool as ....
8 as quiet as ....
9 as cold as ....
10 as fresh as ....

2 Complete the sentences with the past form of the verbs given.

gasp • groan • mutter • shriek • sigh
whine • whisper • yell

1 'Can anyone hear me?' .... Max from inside the cellar.
2 'I can't run any more,' .... Susie as she sank to her knees.
3 'There's a rat!' .... Jenny and she ran out of the room.
4 'I don't think we will ever be friends,' .... Mason.
5 'Let's meet up later, but don't tell anyone,' .... Pat.
6 'I want some chocolate. Get me some chocolate,' .... the little boy at the supermarket checkout.
7 'I hate maths,' John .... to himself, but no one paid him any attention.
8 'Oh, no! Not more homework!' .... the students loudly.

3 Read the story. Which picture is not in the story? Order the other pictures.

A GOOD DEED

A

It was a cold, dark evening and my dad, who was a cab driver at the time, was getting close to the end of his shift. He hadn't had a particularly good evening so far. When business was slow in the evening, Dad would often go to a café and that's where he was. He was sitting and chatting to a mate when suddenly the door burst open. In the doorway stood a short man with a face as red as a lobster, wearing a chef's hat and apron. He looked worried to death. 'Quickly,' he yelled. 'Who's the cab driver?' 'Me,' said my dad. 'I need a cab, now this very moment! But I haven't got any money with me!' My dad's a kind man and he agreed to drive the man.

The chef wanted to be driven to the Ritz Hotel. There was a dinner there that night, but the chef who was going to cook the meal had fallen ill. 'I'm the replacement, but I was in such a hurry I forgot my wallet,' he explained. 'And there are some very important people there.' Dad drove through the London streets as fast as lightning! As soon as they arrived at the Ritz, the chef asked for my dad's card and then rushed into the hotel. Dad forgot all about the little chef until several days later when he received a letter in the post. There was a cheque for three hundred pounds and a handwritten letter thanking him for his kind act, signed by Prince William. It had been his party!

B

C

D

4 Read the story again. Find and underline examples of:

1 a simile
2 a way of speaking from 2
3 a variety of past tenses
4 inversion for dramatic effect
5 linkers and expressions of time and sequence

5 You are going to write a story with the title 'A good deed'. Use some of the ideas in the box or your own ideas. Copy and complete the plan with your notes.

an airport • a bag of shopping • a café
a car park • an expensive handbag
a puppy • a roll of banknotes

The beginning	The middle	The end

6 Write your story. Use the Writing bank in the Student's Book and the checklist below.

Have you used:

- a range of vocabulary and tenses?
- good paragraphing?
- correct linking devices?
- interesting language?
- the correct number of words?

Grammar

1 Complete the sentences with the correct form of the verbs given.

1 I .... (sit) here thinking about this essay for half an hour and I've still got no ideas.

2 Karen .... (text) Alison in class when the teacher .... (notice) and .... (take) her phone away!

3 We .... (drive) to London for the concert, but at the last minute we .... (change) our minds and .... (take) the train instead.

4 On the news yesterday I .... (see) that the police .... (arrest) a man the previous day because he .... (drive) along the motorway in the wrong direction!

5 I .... (be) fascinated by psychology since I .... (go) to a talk on it a couple of months ago.

6 By the 1980s the university .... (attract) students from all over Europe and lecturers, too.

2 Complete the story with the correct form of the verbs given.

When I **(a)** .... (wake up) that morning, sunlight **(b)** .... (stream) through my window and I realised that I **(c)** .... (forget) to set the alarm the night before. I **(d)** .... (definitely be) late on my first day at the new job. I quickly **(e)** .... (shower), **(f)** .... (eat) some toast and **(g)** .... (run) out of the front door. Another problem! I **(h)** .... (have) a puncture on my bike while I **(i)** .... (ride) home from college the previous afternoon and, of course, I **(j)** .... (be) too busy to fix it.
OK. I **(k)** .... (look) at my watch. Just enough time to catch the 9.15. I **(l)** .... (run) to the bus stop when I remembered that I **(m)** .... (leave) my wallet on the kitchen table. I started back to the house. The morning **(n)** .... (go) very well at all. And it **(o)** .... (get) any better. There on my doorstep was the postman. He **(p)** .... (look) cross. 'I **(q)** .... (ring) this bell for ages,' he complained and handed me a bunch of letters. They **(r)** .... (be) all bills and I **(s)** .... (see) from the red writing that they were overdue. The postman smiled nastily. 'Have a nice day,' he said and **(t)** .... (walk) off, humming.

3 Find and correct the mistakes in the sentences.

1 When my mum was young they would drive on the left in Sweden.

2 My brother is always giving me lifts in his new car. It's great!

3 Tina often gets corrected in class because she will use the wrong endings for the verbs.

4 My mum was getting cross with my sister because whenever she had money she would spend it on other people.

5 We didn't used to live in the city centre when we first moved here.

Vocabulary

1 Complete the sentences with the correct form of the words given.

1 The twins had a big .... about who should drive the new car first. **argue**

2 Cathy got quite upset about her .... to get into university last month. **fail**

3 .... is a basic human right. **free**

4 Have you ever noticed the .... between Jamie and his brother? **similar**

5 Candidates are marked on their grammatical .... and range of vocabulary. **accurate**

2 Complete the sentences with the correct part of the body.

1 Why has Dave been giving me the cold .... all morning?

2 My dad has always been under my mum's ....! She's definitely the boss.

3 I hate it when your friends go behind your .... and gossip about you.

4 Don't pull my ....! I know you haven't forgotten my birthday.

5 Best friends will always stick their .... out for each other.

3 Use similes to complete the sentences.

1 Hank was .... and managed to lift the car easily.

2 I had a good night's sleep and woke up the next morning ....

3 The new girl said very little. She was ....

4 I couldn't understand the explanation at all. It was ....

5 Working out where the robbers had gone was .... and we traced them immediately.

4 Circle the correct alternative.

1 Margie *yelled/muttered* loudly when she tripped and fell on the pavement.

2 Jack *whined/whispered* because he didn't want the others to hear what he was saying to me.

3 Penny *muttered/gasped* when she dived into the water because it was so cold!

4 Tim *muttered/groaned* when he realised he had an exam that day.

5 'It's not fair – that's my toy!' the little boy *whined/whispered*.

2 Road trips

Reading

1a VOCABULARY Find words in the word search to create compound nouns with the following words.

1 ....way
2 ....licence
3 seat..........................
4 ....signs
5 ....station
6 ....wheel
7 traffic..........................
8 ....lights
9 round..........................
10 ....limit

G	X	E	J	S	M	F	X	P	T	U
R	S	Z	A	B	O	U	T	A	U	T
U	O	T	M	E	T	T	T	S	V	R
C	B	A	C	L	O	N	M	I	K	A
F	L	O	D	T	R	S	F	M	P	F
S	P	E	E	D	E	Z	I	L	I	F
Y	E	T	S	L	A	Q	D	F	E	I
S	T	E	E	R	I	N	G	R	E	C
A	R	E	O	X	L	A	O	P	F	M
G	O	S	U	C	R	P	S	Z	J	D
I	L	S	D	R	I	V	I	N	G	P

1b Complete the questions with the correct compound nouns.

1 What's the .... on the road outside this building? Is it 50 kph?
2 How many .... are there in your family car?
3 When did you last get stuck in a ....?
4 Does your local .... sell things other than fuel?
5 How many sets of .... are there between this building and your home?
6 Can you describe four different .... on motorways?

2 Read the magazine article, ignoring the gaps, and answer these questions.

1 How many people went on the trip?
2 What record did Mike want to break?

3 Read the article again. Choose from the sentences (a–h) the one which best fits each gap (1–8).

a 'The Mayan cultures in the Guatemalan highlands, the ruins of Palenque and Tikal, and riding up to the rim of a volcano in Nicaragua were also amazing,' he says.
b None of them had any experience of doing this kind of trip so they needed to prepare carefully.
c These ranged from snow and ice in permafrost areas to extreme heat and humidity in Central America.
d When he got back to Australia he was only 19 years old, making him the youngest person to ride around the world by over four years.
e But Mike Schram is not your average teenager.
f Despite having to follow these strict rules, however, Mike had another aim.
g Mike wanted to encourage them to do more with their life by writing about his experiences in a blog.
h But they also learnt about how to avoid potential dangers, and how to deal with practical problems.

4 CRITICAL THINKING

Which of these statements do you think are good (G) or bad (B) advice for a young person planning a trip?

1 You should avoid dangerous countries, e.g. countries where there are wars. G/B
2 It isn't necessary to plan in any detail. Go with the flow! G/B
3 You'll have a better time if you go on your own. G/B
4 You ought to do a lot of research before you go. G/B
5 You don't need to organise all the finances before you go. You can get money on the way. G/B

5 Match the underlined words with the definitions.

1 the clothes and equipment you need for an activity ....
2 the most interesting, exciting or impressive parts of something ....
3 started a journey ....
4 a person or business that pays money to support something as a way of advertising ....
5 put off doing something/persuaded not to do something ....
6 continued trying to achieve something difficult ....
7 deal successfully with a difficult situation ....
8 something that makes you worried because you think it will be difficult or dangerous ....

THE TRIP OF A LIFETIME

The dream of many teenagers is to pass their exams, go to university and get a good job. (1) .... His dream was to become the youngest person to ride around the world on a motorbike. And so in 2012, he set off from Australia at the age of just 16, alongside his parents, who had allowed him to go on the condition that they came, too.

Mike made the decision to leave because he wanted to live his life to the full. But there was another factor involved too. While he was growing up, he saw many teenagers doing things that they shouldn't and getting in trouble. **(2)** ....
So he hoped that his trip would inspire others, as well as being an amazing adventure for him and his family.

Organising a long trip like this and the dangers involved might have put most people off, but the Schrams persevered. **(3)** .... They read travel guides, watched videos and collected as much information as they could. This included hearing many daunting stories about terrible accidents and how dangerous these trips could be.

(4) .... They had to get all the gear they needed and decide on their route, get visas and organise shipping the bikes where necessary. Financing the trip was also a challenge. They didn't want to have an official sponsor because they wanted to show that anyone could do a trip like this. In the end, they decided to sell their house to pay for it. One way of saving money was their decision to camp, so they didn't need to pay for hotels. Finally, and most importantly, Mike had to get a motorbike and a motorbike licence!

To set a world record, Mike had to achieve a true circumnavigation. This means you have to go all the way round the Earth. You must start and finish at the same point, travel in one general direction and reach two antipodes (two diametrically opposite places on Earth) and cover a minimum of 40,000 kilometres. **(5)** .... He wanted to travel slowly and take the time to really experience each different country. The Schrams planned their route to avoid main highways, hoping the smaller roads might mean a more interesting trip.

While he was growing up, he saw many teenagers doing things that they shouldn't and getting in trouble.

They rode through most of the seven continents and travelled thousands of kilometres. Among the places their route took them were New Zealand, Canada, Alaska, the US, Mexico, Belize, Guatemala, Honduras, Nicaragua, Costa Rica, The Netherlands, Belgium and the UK and northern Europe. Before they left, Mike's parents were concerned about how he would cope. They needn't have worried. Mike was young but he certainly proved himself highly capable in extreme conditions. **(6)** .... Mike also faced the danger of bears, crazy drivers and difficult border crossings. He had long days riding and he had to learn about bike repair. Although some people felt Mike's parents shouldn't have let him take this trip at such a young age, he showed that he could deal with the challenge.

For Mike, the highlights of the trip were the stunningly beautiful National Parks in Canada and the US, the amazing people he met in every country and the fantastic food in Mexico, as well as the tradition of motor biking in the UK. **(7)** .... He was glad he wasn't deterred by the alarming stories people told him when he was planning the trip. Of course, there were tricky moments, but in general it was a hugely positive experience. 'If you believe half the rumours about foreign countries, then you can't go anywhere. Once you're in those countries, the reality is often very different. People are basically the same wherever you go.'

Mike managed to achieve his dream. **(8)** .... Mike's parents never had any doubt that he would be able to achieve his goal and there is no doubt he is an inspiration to teenagers around the world. The only question is, what will he do next?

1 Match the verbs in bold (1–10) with the uses (a–h).

1 They **had to** get all the gear they needed. ....
2 You **must** start and finish at the same point. ....
3 They **didn't need to** pay for hotels. ....
4 None of them had any experience and they **needed to** prepare themselves. ....
5 Mike's parents were concerned, but they **needn't have** worried. ....
6 Some people felt his parents **shouldn't have** let him do the trip. ....
7 Mike **was allowed to** follow his dream. ....
8 Young people **mustn't** waste their lives. ....
9 Before travelling you **should** find out about the places you want to visit. ....
10 Circumnavigation means you **have to** go all the way round the Earth. ....

a present obligation or necessity
b past obligation or necessity
c past lack of obligation
d past things which are not obligatory or necessary
e present prohibition
f present advice
g past criticism
h past permission

2 Choose the correct use of the words in bold in these sentences.

1 You **mustn't drive** over 30 kilometres per hour in the town centre.
A obligation B permission C prohibition
2 We **don't need to get** a new car yet. This one's fine.
A lack of necessity B lack of obligation C criticism
3 Jacky **ought to take** a few more lessons before her test.
A obligation B advice C permission
4 You **don't have to get** all the questions right in the written part of the driving test.
A criticism B advice C lack of obligation
5 I **must remember** to lend Hannah my Highway Code book tomorrow.
A obligation B advice C permission
6 With this car insurance I'**m allowed to** drive my dad's car, too.
A prohibition B permission C advice
7 You **shouldn't have** the radio too loud while you're driving. Can you turn it down?
A lack of obligation B prohibition C criticism
8 You'**d better hurry up** because the driving instructor is here.
A obligation B advice C permission
9 I'm sorry but you **can't park** outside our gate.
A lack of obligation B criticism C prohibition
10 I **have to return** the car to my dad before six or he'll be mad at me!
A advice B obligation C permission

3 Find and correct the mistakes in the sentences. One sentence is correct.

1 I needn't have gone to the bank later because Mum lent me some money yesterday.
2 We don't have to get the train to school today because Dad's giving us a lift.
3 They mustn't have put that pedestrian crossing there because it's much too dangerous.
4 It's going to rain soon so you've got to bring your books in from the garden.
5 We mustn't finish this project on traffic congestion until the end of the week.
6 According to the sign we may not have driven through the town centre yesterday, so we took a different route.
7 You hadn't better hand in your essay before you've checked it.
8 In the driving test I ought to have answered a lot of questions about road signs, which were really hard.

GRAMMAR CHALLENGE

4 Complete the email to a friend telling her about taking your driving test earlier today.

Hi Ellie,

I took my driving test today but I failed. I did everything wrong! I **(a)** *shouldn't have gone* (go) the wrong way round a roundabout. I **(b)** .... (turn) left, but instead I turned right. I **(c)** .... (stop) at the traffic lights, but I didn't. I stopped at the pedestrian crossing, but I **(d)** .... (stop) because there was nobody there! I **(e)** .... (not listen) to Seb's advice – I didn't study and I couldn't answer most of the examiner's questions. I **(f)** .... (study) harder next time! I **(g)** .... (allowed/finish) the test because I went over the speed limit. I **(h)** .... (notice) the road sign, but I was too busy talking!

Love Sue

1 Complete the questions with the correct form of *make*, *take* or *do*.

1 Is there a topic you'd like to .... a course in?
2 What have you recently .... some research into?
3 Have you ever .... a complaint about a journey on public transport?
4 Which household chores do you hate .... at home?
5 If you were given a lot of money would you .... a risk with it to make more?
6 When did you last .... a mistake in English?

2 Match the halves to make sentences.

1 The learner driver was going to crash so the instructor had to ....
2 When you're looking at which courses to study at university it's so important to ....
3 You can have this old bicycle if you can ....
4 When they get computers installed in every classroom it will really ....
5 We've got a new boss and he's going to ....
6 I often let my baby brother play in my room because I know he won't ....

a make changes.
b make use of it.
c make the right choice.
d do any harm.
e take control.
f make a difference.

3 Replace the phrases in bold with an expression using *make*, *take* or *do* so that the sentence means the same.

1 The politician **said some interesting things** about the new driving test.
The politician made some interesting comments about the new driving test.
2 When the rain started we **sheltered** under a big tree.
....
3 Helen **had a good idea** about where we should go for a picnic.
....
4 The man **objected** to Dad's comment about his car and drove off angrily.
....
5 I **tried several times** to start the car but with no success.
....
6 I **looked online for information** about the history of motoring for the project.
....

4 LISTENING 03 **Listen to an interview. What does Teresa like about her job?**

5 03 **Listen again and choose the correct answers.**

1 Teresa ...
a always wanted to be a mountain climber or firefighter.
b would prefer to be a window cleaner of a skyscraper.
c loves her job despite the risks it involves.

2 Teresa says that when she started her job ...
a she had many problems because people weren't used to female instructors.
b a few people were surprised because they thought she was going to be a man.
c most of her learners preferred having a female teacher to a male teacher.

3 According to Teresa, learning to drive nowadays is ...
a harder because there is far more traffic than there used to be.
b more difficult because you have to make more instant decisions.
c just the same as before, nothing has changed at all.

4 In the example of road rage ...
a the man refused to move his car from the junction.
b she felt angrier with the man than frightened of him.
c the man was probably worried about getting to the hospital.

5 Teresa thinks that ...
a you should never listen to music in the car.
b most accidents are caused by distractions in the car.
c it's OK to eat a small simple snack in the car.

VOCABULARY EXTENSION

6 Circle the correct alternative.

1 When I borrowed Mum's car, I *made/took* the most of the opportunity and drove to the beach.
2 Thanks for a great party. I have to *make/do* tracks because I have to be home by 11 pm.
3 I recently *made/did* my friend a favour and helped him with his project.
4 Jim invited me out, but I had to *do/take* a rain check because I already had other plans.
5 I haven't been shopping so we'll have to make *do/take* with what's left in the fridge.
6 My dad never *does/takes* my mum for granted. He always thanks her for the things she does.

1 Write the verbs in bold next to the uses (1–6).

a There **can't be** too many people who want to risk getting into a car with someone who's never driven before.

b That **must have been** very frightening.

c It **can't have been** easy being a female instructor then.

d Being worried **could well have been** the reason he behaved like that.

e It **must be** much more difficult to learn to drive on today's roads.

f That **might be** the best reason for doing this job!

1 something in the present we are 90% certain is true ....

2 something in the present that is possible ....

3 something in the present we are 90% certain is not true ....

4 something in the past that we are 90% certain was true ....

5 something in the past that was possible ....

6 something in the past that we are 90% certain was not true ....

2 Complete the sentences with the correct modal verb *must, might/could* or *can't*.

1 'David speaks excellent Spanish. Is he from Spain?'
'David? His parents are from London, so he .... be Spanish!'

2 'Have you found Sarah yet?'
'She .... be in her bedroom, I've looked everywhere else.'

3 'I think Sam lives in that house.'
'No, he .... live there, he told me he lived in a flat.'

4 'Is the dog in the garden?'
'I'm not sure, it .... be in the garden, or perhaps it's in the living room.'

5 'Do the police know who did it?'
'They have two suspects. It .... be John Smith or it .... be Rob Brown.'

3 Complete the sentences with a modal verb and the correct form of the verbs given.

1 Lucy .... (go) to the sports centre, all her sports gear is here.

2 I thought I saw Liam in town yesterday, but it .... (be) him because he was ill and stayed in bed all day.

3 I can't find my purse. I .... (leave) it at home I suppose, but I thought I'd put it in my bag. I hope it hasn't been stolen!

4 Chris .... (arrive) home by now, it only takes him ten minutes to walk there and he left 20 minutes ago. I'll phone him now.

5 The train .... (leave)! It isn't supposed to leave for another five minutes.

6 Steve and Marie .... (have) an argument. They both look angry and I heard them shouting.

4 Complete the sentences with a modal verb and the correct form of these verbs.

be (x2) • go (x2) • like • lose

1 I can't find my glasses anywhere. I .... them.

2 That girl .... Kate's sister. Her sister is tall and that girl is very short.

3 Mark .... biscuits – he's eaten the whole packet!

4 Cathy .... to sleep late last night, she can't stop yawning.

5 Noel isn't here. He .... at Tom's house, I'll text him and find out.

6 Pete .... to the party, but I'm not sure. There were so many people there.

GRAMMAR CHALLENGE

5 Rewrite the sentences with the words given. Do not change the meaning.

1 You didn't see Joe in the street this morning, I was with him at home. **can't**
You .... this morning, I was with him at home.

2 Sarah started working three hours ago. She is still working now. **for**
Sarah .... three hours.

3 Perhaps that boy is Luke's cousin. **be**
That boy .... Luke's cousin.

4 I often went to the beach in summer when I was a child. **go**
When I was a child, I .... in summer.

5 Mike talked to Kiera before he phoned me. **already**
Mike .... when he phoned me.

6 The teacher said we mustn't use dictionaries in the exam. **to**
The teacher said we .... use dictionaries in the exam.

1 LISTENING 04 **Look at the four photos and listen to David's description. Which photo (A–D) is he describing?**

A

B

C

D

2 04 **Listen again. Are the sentences True (T) or False (F)?**

1 David thinks the people are tourists. T/F
2 He is sure they are on a city break. T/F
3 He thinks they chose this form of transport because it's cheap. T/F
4 He would be happy to try this kind of tour. T/F

3 Read a description of one of the other photos and complete it with modal verbs and the correct form of the verbs given. Sometimes more than one modal is possible. Which photo is it?

'The photo is of some people with bicycles in the countryside. It **(a)** .... (take) by a friend or it **(b)** .... (take) by a professional photographer as part of an advertising campaign. The people **(c)** .... (be) members of the same family because they're not all the same age. They **(d)** .... (know) the area I suppose. I'm not sure what they're looking at, but it **(e)** .... (be) interesting as they're all looking intently! As to why they're here – well, they **(f)** .... (be) on holiday or they **(g)** .... (decide) to go for a cycle ride on a Sunday afternoon. I think they **(h)** .... (enjoy) themselves because the area looks quiet without a lot of noise or traffic and the weather looks good, too.'

4 Look at the other two photos not described in 1 or 3. Complete the table with your ideas.

	Photo	Photo ......
1 Where are they?		
2 Who are they?		
3 What are they doing?		
4 How are they feeling?		
5 Why are they in these places?		
6 Why did they choose this form of transport?		

5 Write sentences to compare two photos in 4 using the words or phrases given.

1 both ....
2 whereas ....
3 however ....
4 not as … as ....
5 one significant difference ....
6 it's hard to say, but ....

6 Read the task and write your answer. Use words and phrases from the Speaking bank in the Student's Book.

The photos show people using different forms of transport on holiday. Compare and contrast two of the photos and say:

- why the people have chosen these forms of transport
- how they might be feeling
- which situation you would prefer to be in, and why.

1 Read the essay title and notes. Rewrite the underlined parts of the sentences with more formal expressions in your notebooks.

'All city centres should be pedestrianised.'

1 I'm sure that pedestrianising city centres would be a good idea.
I am certain that …
2 A lot of people think that it would be too expensive.
3 I've thought for ages that the air must be really polluted in the city.
4 There's no way you can justify putting it off.
5 I don't think there's anything to show that heavy traffic is really damaging the buildings.
6 It might be inconvenient for some people, but I still think it would be a good thing.
7 There are no two ways about it. City centres should be pedestrianised.

2 Read the essay. Complete the text with the words and phrases in the box.

a strong case • firstly • in addition • in conclusion • in spite of • secondly • strongly • surely

It is widely believed that for environmental and safety reasons the time has now come for city centres to be pedestrianised, banning all non-essential traffic. I certainly believe that there is **(a)** .... for doing this.

(b) ...., we can see in many cities the terrible result of years of heavy traffic. Wonderful old buildings have cracks in their walls because they have been shaken to their foundations by the increasing number of heavy vehicles rumbling past. **(c)** .... to this, the facades of buildings have grown dingy and need continual repainting because of the discolouration caused by the fumes from cars.

(d) ...., if the state of the buildings reflects the state of the air that people who work, shop or walk through city centres are breathing in, health concerns must also be a major issue. In many big cities, pedestrians are forced to wear face masks to protect themselves from the polluted air. This is **(e)** .... unacceptable. **(f)** .... the cost involved and the inconvenience caused to people travelling through cities, I am convinced that it would be a worthwhile investment for the future. To my mind, there is no question that without this action, the anticipated increase in traffic over the next 20 years could result in total gridlock for our city centres.

(g) ...., I must say that I **(h)** .... believe that our cities must change with the times. I really hope that within a few years all city centres will become areas for pedestrians only.

3 Read the essay title and notes. Complete the table with the notes (1–7).

'Speed cameras are not a good way to make our roads safer.'

1 People slow down when they see a camera and then speed up again after. They aren't a serious deterrent.
2 When there are more cameras, people get into the habit of driving more slowly.
3 Speed cameras are a deterrent. If you know you will be fined or even lose your licence, then you slow down.
4 It all depends on road conditions. The vast majority of drivers know when it is better to slow down.
5 Speed cameras are not effective. They are just a way for the government to make money.
6 Drivers react much more positively to the automatic signs that flash up when you are going over the speed limit. They are a good reminder.
7 There are fewer accidents in areas with speed cameras.

For	Against
	1

4 Plan an essay on the statement in 3. Make notes following the paragraph plan below.

Paragraph 1: Introduction. Talk about the situation/ meaning of the statement and indicate your opinion
Paragraph 2: Main points supporting your opinion
Paragraph 3: Additional points
Paragraph 4: Points against your opinion and your reaction to these
Paragraph 5: Conclusion. Summarise/restate opinion

5 Write your essay. Use the Writing bank in the Student's Book and the checklist below.

After your first draft:
- Check for spelling and grammar mistakes
- Check for correct paragraphing

Grammar

1 Circle the correct alternative.

1 You mustn't/don't have to write in ink. Please use pencil.
2 When I saw Mark this morning, I must have/ought to have apologised to him, but I was too embarrassed.
3 We're supposed to/needed to have finished the project by tomorrow but there's no way we can.
4 We didn't need to wait/needn't have waited for Jack to arrive so we left straight after dinner.
5 You shouldn't have/had better have spoken to Susie like that. It made her really upset.
6 We don't have to/aren't allowed to see the results before they're put up on the notice board.

2 Complete the second sentence so that it has a similar meaning to the first sentence, using a modal structure.

1 I'm positive Jane passed her driving test.
Jane .... her driving test.
2 I'm pretty sure that's not Earl's sister. She's not blonde.
That .... Earl's sister.
3 I imagine that you're pleased with your exam results!
You .... pleased with your exam results!
4 It's possible that the film on TV tonight is a repeat.
The film on TV tonight .... a repeat.
5 I'm almost certain the show hasn't started already.
The show .... already.

3 Correct the mistakes.

1 You must see Lewis at the party on Saturday night, he was away all last weekend.
2 I have been taking my driving test three times.
3 I handed in my project yesterday, but I didn't need to hand it in so early – the deadline is next week!
4 Mark ought to have spoken to Megan like that. It was really rude.
5 The film was already starting when we arrived, so we missed the first ten minutes.

4 Complete the dialogue with an appropriate modal verb and the correct form of the verbs given.

A: Sorry I'm late. I **(a)** .... (run) all the way because I missed the bus.
B: You **(b)** .... (rush). Gemma isn't here yet. She **(c)** .... (leave) school early – she **(d)** .... (wait) until the end of lessons, even though she'd finished all her work.
A: That's unfair. They **(e)** .... (make) her stay. We **(f)** .... (run) if we want to catch the 4.15 train.
B: It's OK. We **(g)** .... (be) there until five. We **(h)** .... (sign in) at 4.45, but they won't mind if we don't.

Vocabulary

1 Complete the sentences with the correct words to make compound nouns.

1 The authorities are now talking about making it compulsory to have seat.................... for dogs in cars!
2 While I was driving the ....wheel came off in my hands! It was very scary.
3 What's the speed.................... on this road?
4 There are so many road.................... along this road that it can be quite distracting.
5 All the petrol.................... in our area have just put up their prices.

2 Complete the sentences with the correct form of *make, take* or *do*.

1 I .... some research into the subject of electric cars and I found some interesting facts.
2 The service in the restaurant was so poor that we had to .... a complaint.
3 If you .... any mistakes we can go over them before the next test.
4 It's raining heavily! Let's .... cover under that tree.
5 Martin .... offence because Jackie said he could improve his pronunciation.
6 When I .... a serious comment about the film Sue just laughed.
7 Surely eating one or two biscuits a day isn't going to .... you any harm?
8 The event .... place last week and hundreds of people went to it.

3 Choose the correct answers.

1 Our teacher really .... an interest in all the students.
A does B takes C makes
2 'Stop immediately!' the policeman .... to the robber.
A whispered B whined C yelled
3 Who .... the household chores in your house?
A does B takes C makes
4 Matt wasn't serious, he was just pulling my ....
A thumb B neck C leg
5 I was late because I got stuck in a .... jam.
A traffic B road C motorway
6 He failed his driving .... because he tried to drive the wrong way around the roundabout!
A licence B test C exam
7 I've decided which course to do at university. I hope I've .... the right choice!
A done B made C taken

Reading

1 For questions 1–9, choose from the three Internet users (A–C). Each person may be chosen more than once.

Which person

- is relieved that a problem he/she had online has been sorted out? **1** ....
- thinks social networking sites are a waste of time? **2** ....
- feels that their online activity has helped them in real life? **3** ....
- has stopped using Twitter because he/she wasn't getting anything out of it? **4** ....
- has met people he/she would not have met otherwise? **5** ....
- feels he/she has grown personally as a result of his/her online activity? **6** ....
- is confident using technology for a variety of purposes? **7** ....
- limited the amount of time he/she spent online? **8** ....
- has used it to remain in contact with people he/she wouldn't have had time to communicate with? **9** ....

SOCIAL NETWORK NEWS

HOME | TOP STORIES | COMMENTS | SIGN IN | CONTACT US | SEARCH

A Jacky141

For me, social networking is the best possible use of the Internet. It's by far the best way to keep in touch with people – I'm sure that without it I would have lost contact with loads of people because there just aren't enough hours in the day to talk to everyone you want to. It's easy to do – I'm not a computer geek or anything and even I can tweet on Twitter, not that I use it because I found it pretty boring. But I love updating my Facebook page! It's difficult to explain, but I suppose it's like being part of a group without having to organise things. I'm also a member of an online community for people interested in my hobby – politics! Quite honestly, I'd be lost without the online contact because my friends hate it. We discuss politics online at all hours – sometimes I'm up all night, typing, thinking, scrolling, debating. The people I link up with are from all over the world – people I'd never get the chance to meet in real life, all offering different views based on different experiences. Other people I know link up with people just as I do, but with different interests. I couldn't live without my virtual social life!

♥Like ↰Reply <Share

B Freddie

I understand why people might enjoy social networking sites like Twitter, but they just aren't my thing. My online community is through the game World of Warcraft. Not quite the same as a social networking site or online discussion group I know, but for me it's really like being in another world with loads of new friends where you can do everything and anything you've ever wanted to do. It's fun, too! Last week someone hacked into my account and I couldn't get back into the game – I was absolutely devastated. Luckily, I was able to sort it out – phew! I've increased my account security to stop that ever happening again.

At first I was a bit dubious about spending so much time on the computer because you hear about people getting addicted. Anyway, I decided to only play at certain times. After I'd been playing for a month, I realised it's been very good for me. I'm quite shy and having an avatar helped me make friends in a way I wouldn't have been able to in real life. Learning to negotiate with others has been very character building. My mum was worried it would take over my physical social life but I think it's been the opposite. I'm more confident now and I enjoy going out more.

♥Like ↰Reply <Share

C StuMacT

I'm sorry, but I just don't get it. OK, I'm sixtyish but I keep up-to-date with the latest technology and I can find my way round the Internet quite happily. I'm always Googling something or other. What I can't understand is the attraction of these social networking sites. I did try going on Facebook and for a while I suppose it was a bit of a novelty but after a bit I just got fed up with all the junk that's on there. I mean, you have to wade through tons of mindless gossip to find any interesting comments. Why is it that people want to tell the world about the most mundane moments of their lives? Give me a break! The only thing that has anything going for it is Twitter. I find it fascinating to follow some people because at least there are some intelligent debates going on. You can find the thoughts of some of the world's greatest thinkers in art, business, politics and technology, all at your fingertips. I love the fact you can see things they're thinking that never end up in books or articles. Of course, I don't follow celebrities where all they tweet about is what they've been doing!

♥Like ↰Reply <Share

Writing

2 Choose one of these two writing tasks. Write between 120 and 180 words.

1 You have had a class discussion about making cities more bike-friendly. Your teacher has now asked you to write an essay giving your opinion on the following statement:
'Bike lanes should be a part of all roads in towns and cities.'

2 Write a story which begins with these words:
I had been looking forward to doing this journey for months, but it turned out to be the worst experience of my life!

Use of English

3 Read the text and decide which answer (A, B, C or D) best fits each gap.

To my **(1)** ...., the Inca Trail is one of the best treks in the world. **(2)** .... the four-day trek, you'll have the opportunity to see beautiful mountain scenery, cloud-forest and tropical jungle. It's worth the 43-kilometre walk when you reach the ruins of Machu Picchu, the mysterious lost city of the Incas. Most people **(3)** .... when they first see this amazing place!

(4) .... it's true that some people do the trek independently, I would recommend going with an organised group. There are plenty of tour companies to choose from. You **(5)** .... do your research before you go and find the best one for you. Having a trained guide can **(6)** .... a huge difference to how much you enjoy the experience. I was lucky enough to go with a great group of people, and we **(7)** .... to help each other at difficult moments. Our guide obviously knew the area and pointed **(8)** .... many fascinating things. Because he was so knowledgeable, everyone **(9)** .... an interest and I certainly learnt a lot that I **(10)** .... before. I will never forget this incredible experience!

	A	B	C	D
1	opinion	mind	thought	idea
2	During	Through	By	For
3	whine	mutter	gasp	whisper
4	Whilst	Moreover	However	Nevertheless
5	could	might	should	don't need to
6	have	make	take	do
7	did	would	used	all
8	in	out	up	down
9	had	made	did	took
10	hadn't known	wasn't knowing	hadn't been knowing	knew

Listening

4 LISTENING 05 **Listen to a radio programme about using satnavs. Choose the best answer.**

1 According to the presenter, ...
   a satnavs often send people to the wrong destination.
   b it is a bad idea to ignore the directions given by the satnav.
   c you should have an idea of how to get to your destination.

2 The two Swedish tourists mistakenly drove to ...
   a a town near their intended destination.
   b a place in the north of Italy instead of in the south.
   c an island off the coast of Italy instead of a town inland.

3 Because of the mistake with the satnav, the shoppers ...
   a did all their shopping in Belgium instead of France.
   b weren't able to do any shopping at all.
   c only had a short time to do all their shopping.

4 The sailor ...
   a did not reach his destination and had to be saved.
   b used maps to navigate in addition to the satnav.
   c was well-prepared for the trip according to the police.

5 The driver of the car in Australia ...
   a noticed the warning sign but ignored it.
   b was worried about driving in the heavy rain.
   c drove down the muddy road despite the rain.

6 Both Rob Jones and Petra Lang ...
   a got stuck in unlikely places while using satnavs.
   b were going to visit friends when the incidents occurred.
   c drove their vehicles into water while using a satnav.

! COMMON MISTAKES

5 Correct the mistakes in the sentences.

1 When I was younger, my family would live in France, but now we live in Scotland.
2 I've taken most things out of my case so it's as light than a feather now.
3 I stayed at home yesterday because it was a study day and I needn't go to school.
4 Kate never has seen that film, but she'd like to one day.
5 Sam's got a red face because he is running for half an hour.
6 The best thing for me about the book has been the characters.
7 I'm happy because I already have passed my driving test.
8 We could as well switch off the TV, this is the worst film I've ever seen.
9 My brother would take my clothes without asking, it drives me crazy!
10 My parents allowed to me to go to the party although it was during the week.
11 I was going to the party, but I had to babysit in the end.
12 Jake isn't here and neither is his bike, he must go for a bike ride.

3 Mind power

Reading

1a VOCABULARY Read the clues and complete the puzzle.

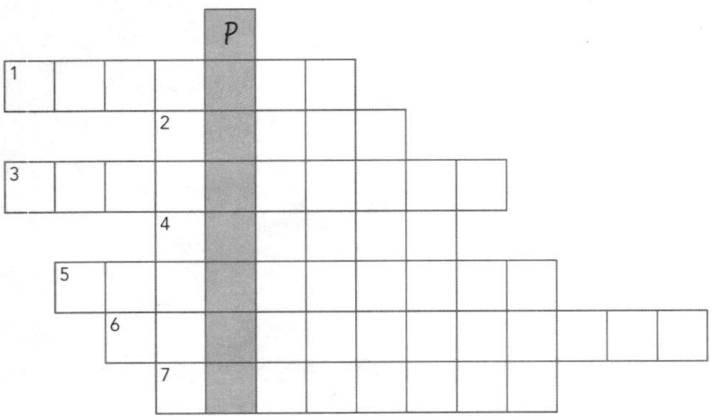

1. Sam's mind often .... He stops concentrating and thinks about other things. (7)
2. I was finding it hard to .... the rules of the game. They were really hard to understand. (5)
3. Kate is able to express her thoughts clearly. She's very .... (10)
4. I met Mark 20 years ago, but I can still .... the first moment I saw him. (6)
5. The tourists were totally lost and they didn't understand us. They looked really .... (10)
6. I .... for languages. I find it really easy to learn them. (4, 1, 4, 3)
7. We've got a history test tomorrow. I have to .... all these names and dates. (8)

1b Rewrite the words in italics with the correct form of the words and phrases from 1a.

1. My mind *gets distracted* in class when it's sunny.
2. When I started learning English we had to *learn* a list of ten new words every evening.
3. My brother, Mark, *has a natural talent for* maths.
4. I didn't *understand* what the teacher was talking about.
5. It was a totally new situation and I was *confused and not certain what to do.*
6. My teacher is *good at explaining things clearly.*
7. It's important not to *see* difficult tasks as negative.
8. I can't *remember* people's names but I always remember their faces.

2 Read the article and choose the best title.

a How robots were invented
b Will robots ever be more intelligent than humans?
c The relationship between humans and machines

3 Read the article again and choose the best answer.

1. Ray Kurzweil believes that …
   a by 2029 robots will still be less intelligent than humans.
   b robots will never be able to make jokes.
   c robots will never behave like humans.
   d robots will be cleverer than humans in the future.
2. According to the article, Capek's play ...
   a featured robots that did the same work as humans.
   b raises interesting questions about artificial beings.
   c wasn't the first one to use the word 'robot'.
   d shows that artificial beings are not just fiction.
3. Modern robots ...
   a no longer do simple repetitive tasks.
   b only do things that humans can do.
   c can think and use words like humans.
   d do many different tasks for humans.
4. In 2014, a computer ...
   a was able to convince a child that it was a person.
   b managed to talk to only 33% of the judges.
   c showed it could convince people it was a human.
   d failed to convince anyone that it could interact with humans.
5. Robots ...
   a are starting to learn from their experiences.
   b can produce better paintings than humans.
   c will never be able to compose music as well as humans.
   d cannot yet predict what humans might do.
6. The writer argues that ...
   a robots will never be more intelligent than humans.
   b it is possible robots may achieve consciousness.
   c scientists will never achieve artificial intelligence.
   d robots can already think like humans.

4 CRITICAL THINKING

What evidence would you use to support the view that robots could think for themselves and become more intelligent than humans?

5 Match the underlined words with the definitions.

1. forming a unified whole in a logical or pleasing way ....
2. communicating with or reacting to ....
3. produced the features of something in a way that seems real but is not ....
4. did or became better than ....
5. a set of rules for solving problems or doing calculations ....
6. not beautiful to listen to ....

For most scientists, it is not a question of if robots will become more intelligent than humans, but when.

Ray Kurzweil, Google's director of engineering, is one of the world's leading experts in artificial intelligence and he believes it will happen sooner than expected. Kurzweil has predicted that by 2029 machines won't just be able to think for themselves, they will have surpassed human intelligence. Kurzweil says that by then robots will not only demonstrate intelligent behaviour similar to human beings – for example being able to understand what we say, make jokes and tell stories – but he also expects them to be more intelligent than us.

Robots are a relatively recent invention. The word was invented in 1920 by the playwright Karel Capek for one of his plays. It comes from the Czech word *robota* meaning 'forced labour'. In the play, created beings called robots did all the work that humans didn't want to do. At the time, Capek's idea was pure fiction, but it left us with profound questions: Will machines ever be able to do everything a human can do? Will they ever become intelligent beings?

Today, we use the word robot for machines that are programmed to carry out tasks. In less than a hundred years since Capek dreamt up the idea of beings with artificial intelligence, robots have come a long way. Early robots could only do simple repetitive actions such as building cars, but now they can do a whole range of increasingly complex jobs. They tend to do things that are too dangerous or impossible for humans such as exploring space, going into buildings to locate bombs, or finding objects underwater.

"It is clear that robots are becoming more intelligent and human-like."

Modern robotics is changing the types of tasks robots do and each new generation of robots is increasingly sophisticated. Robots can now navigate, remember and calculate far better than humans. Already, robots are being designed to perform more human-like functions such as caring for the elderly and even being companions to humans.

So why do Kurzweil and other experts think robots will soon be more intelligent than humans? Robots function using computer programs, and the ability of computer programs to 'think' is developing fast. When the supercomputer 'Deep Blue' beat the world chess champion Garry Kasparov in 1997 it was a revolutionary moment. More recently, a computer called 'Watson' beat human challengers in a quiz game on television. Although these programs were limited to specific tasks, they demonstrate that robots can 'think'.

The technology that allows robots to think is developing fast. In 2014, a computer program simulated the role of a 13-year-old Ukrainian boy called Eugene Goostman at a research event. At the event, a group of judges had an online conversation with Eugene and his replies convinced 33% of them that they were chatting to a human. Although the conversation was short and limited, it led experts to believe that soon it will be impossible to know if we are interacting with a human or a machine.

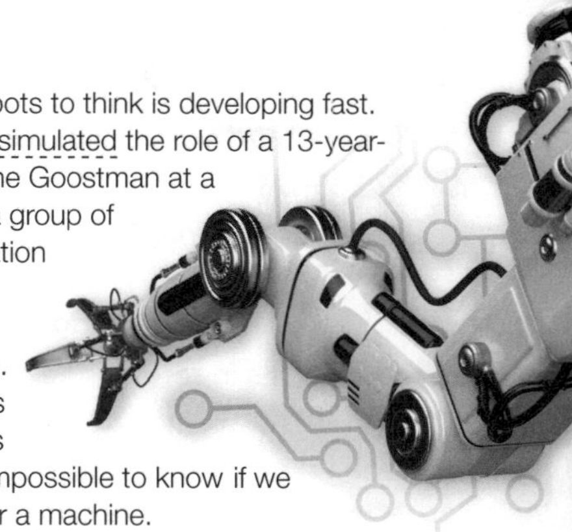

Robots aren't just getting closer to being able to think for themselves, they are now able to learn from their experiences. In 2015, a team of researchers from two British universities developed a robot 'dog' for the blind that can not only detect obstacles, but can also adjust its speed when it senses any resistance or hesitation from the user. In addition, it can predict the user's next actions based on the way they are moving and their previous actions. The robot guide dog is just one example of robots using complex algorithms to learn and to interact with humans.

"Will machines ever be able to do everything a human can do?"

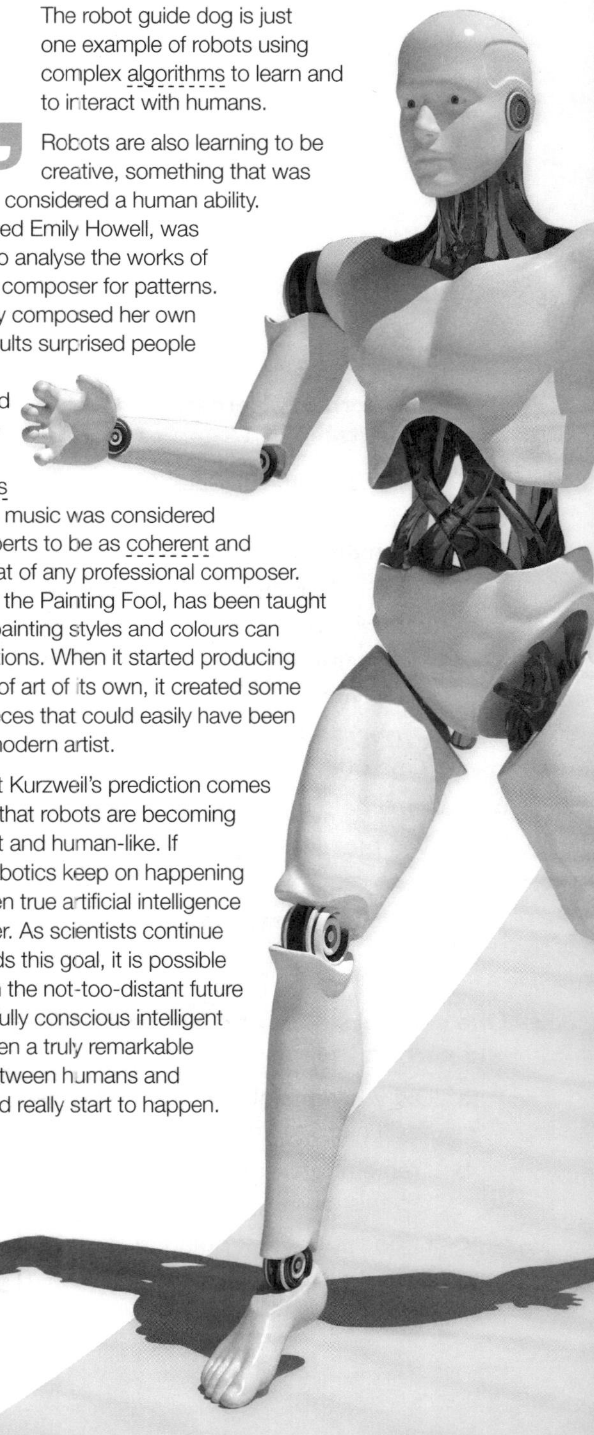

Robots are also learning to be creative, something that was previously only considered a human ability. One robot, called Emily Howell, was programmed to analyse the works of every classical composer for patterns. After this, Emily composed her own music. The results surprised people who thought the robot would only be able to produce basic or unmelodious pieces. Emily's music was considered by musical experts to be as coherent and inventive as that of any professional composer. Another robot, the Painting Fool, has been taught how different painting styles and colours can stimulate emotions. When it started producing original works of art of its own, it created some remarkable pieces that could easily have been painted by a modern artist.

Whether or not Kurzweil's prediction comes true, it is clear that robots are becoming more intelligent and human-like. If advances in robotics keep on happening at this rate, then true artificial intelligence is getting closer. As scientists continue to work towards this goal, it is possible that one day in the not-too-distant future robots will be fully conscious intelligent beings, and then a truly remarkable relationship between humans and machines could really start to happen.

1 Complete the table with the verbs in bold depending on which pattern they follow.

a Robots **tend** to do jobs that are too dangerous for humans.

b By 2029, Kurzweil **expects** robots to be more intelligent than us.

c Robots are also **learning** to be creative.

d If advances in robotics **keep on** happening at this rate, then true artificial intelligence is getting closer.

e When it **started** producing original works of art of its own, it created some remarkable pieces.

f Then a truly remarkable relationship between humans and machines could really **start** to happen.

1 Verb + *-ing* form	2 Verb + to infinitive	3 Verb + *-ing* form or to infinitive with little change or no change of meaning

2 Circle the correct alternative. Add the verbs in bold to the table in 1.

1 I **agreed** to meet/meeting Anna on Saturday night.

2 The price of the sight-seeing tour **includes** to go/going on the London Eye.

3 After a lot of practice, I finally **managed** to remember/remembering all my lines from the play.

4 Dan **recommends** to see/seeing the new Sherlock Holmes film.

5 The suspect **admitted** to be/being near the bank at the time of the robbery.

6 Can you **help** me to make/making the lunch?

7 Do you **feel like** to go/going for a coffee after the lecture?

8 Has anyone **volunteered** to help/helping with the charity event?

3 One sentence a, b, or c has a mistake in it. Find it and correct the mistake.

1 a Did you remember bringing your laptop today? We'll need them in the next lesson.

b I remembered to ask the teacher about the school trip this morning.

c I don't remember doing these exercises. I must have been very tired.

a – remember to bring

2 a I tried to persuade my dad to lend me his car but he said no.

b Have you tried having a milky drink to make you sleepy?

c I must try concentrating more in class and not get distracted.

....

3 a I like to write a translation next to new words because it helps me remember them.

b I like listening to music while I'm travelling.

c I like making a list of grammar mistakes I make in my essays so that I can correct them.

....

4 a My brother can't stop to listen to that song, it's driving me crazy!

b On our way to the concert we had to stop to ask for directions because we got lost.

c My mum stopped working when she had my sister because she needed more time to look after us.

....

5 a After winning his first competition at the age of ten, Leo went on to win many more chess competitions.

b I asked him to stop, but James went on talking about the party for hours!

c Mum asked my brother to help her, but he went on to play his computer game. She wasn't happy!

....

GRAMMAR CHALLENGE

4 Complete the text with the correct form of these verbs.

be • do • enjoy • feel • forget • go • meet • put • say • take • think about

Last week I arranged **(a)** .... Rachel Vines, the actress who is currently starring in the new production of Chekov's *The Cherry Orchard*. She apologised for **(b)** .... late, saying that she had forgotten **(c)** .... the time in her electronic diary. She went on **(d)** .... that her memory was getting worse as she was growing older. In fact, she admitted **(e)** .... her lines several times in the last couple of months. This is obviously a big problem and Rachel wants to stop **(f)** .... theatrical work. She **(g)** .... working in films instead of the theatre. She **(h)** .... that she cannot risk taking on another play. I asked her whether she had tried **(i)** .... to a memory trainer, but she said that she had decided not **(j)** .... that path. Rachel **(k)** .... working in the theatre and has given us some memorable performances.

1 Choose the correct answer to complete the phrasal verbs.

1 In my opinion, people shouldn't look .... on others just because they believe they have a bigger intellect than they do.

A up B off C down

2 The council has come .... with a brilliant new way of recycling rubbish.

A up B on C over

3 I picked .... quite a lot of Greek when we were on holiday in Athens.

A in B down C up

4 I'd like to talk things .... with my family before I make a decision. Is that OK?

A into B about C through

5 Most children think it's really important to be similar to their classmates, otherwise they don't feel that they fit ....

A in B on C up

6 Young people who become famous actors or sports stars need to keep up .... their school work as well.

A on B with C at

2 Complete the blog with one word for each gap.

I'm hopeless at crosswords and I'm sure my family **(a)** .... down on me because I can't **(b)** .... up with answers! They just have to read the clue and the answer **(c)** .... out at them. They don't have to **(d)** .... about it or even **(e)** .... it through with someone. Sometimes it takes me ages to actually **(f)** .... on to what the clue is asking for. They say that after you've been doing crosswords for a while you **(g)** .... up different techniques and it gets easier. They tell me to stop moaning and just **(h)** .... on with it! But all things considered, I think I'll **(i)** .... up trying and **(j)** .... up another sort of mind game. Sudoku sounds more my style!

3 Rewrite the sentences, replacing the objects with pronouns.

1 I must look for my dictionary before I go to school.
I must look for it before I go to school.

2 The students picked up the idea very quickly.
....

3 I took up tennis during the summer holidays.
....

4 I need to get on with my work now so I'll phone you back later.
....

5 After a long discussion we finally hit on a good solution.
....

6 The police are still trying to piece together the story.
....

4 Look at the photos. How do you think these different things help the brain?

5 LISTENING 06 **Listen to five people talking about what they do to improve their brains and keep them healthy. Choose from the list (A–H) what each speaker usually does. There are three extra letters which you do not need to use.**

Speaker 1 ......
Speaker 2 ......
Speaker 3 ......
Speaker 4 ......
Speaker 5 ......

A yoga
B eating the right foods
C solving puzzles
D dancing
E varying routines
F learning a foreign language
G writing by hand
H playing a musical instrument

6 06 **Listen again. Choose from the list (A–G) what each speaker's present occupation is. There are three extra letters which you do not need to use.**

Speaker 1 ......
Speaker 2 ......
Speaker 3 ......
Speaker 4 ......
Speaker 5 ......

A sports instructor
B lawyer
C interpreter
D business person
E bank employee
F dance teacher
G retired person

VOCABULARY EXTENSION

7 Match the words in bold in sentences 1–6 with the definitions (a–f).

1 A walk will **take your mind off** the exam. ......
2 When you go out, **mind** the steps. ......
3 I keep telling myself that I'm not nervous. It's **mind over matter**. ......
4 This computer has got **a mind of its own**. ......
5 I'm sorry I haven't returned your book. It completely **slipped my mind**. ......
6 I **changed my mind** about what to order. ......

a be out of your control
b distract you from
c if you think you can do something it can happen
d be careful of
e make a different decision
f forget something

1 Match the sentences to the correct form (a–c).

1 Doing crosswords **made** me think about the meaning of words. ....
2 I'd **encourage** everyone to learn at least one other language. ....
3 A colleague **persuaded** me to go to salsa classes with her. ....
4 I've **noticed** myself making complex decisions more quickly. ....
5 He'd **overheard** us discussing different ways to relax. ....
6 She **let** me come to one of her classes. ....
7 Music **allows** me to relax. ....
8 I **find** myself doing things on autopilot. ....

a verb + object + *-ing* form
b verb + object + *to* infinitive
c verb + object + infinitive without *to*

2 Choose the correct answers.

1 Reading science fiction books inspired me .... a writer.
A becoming B to become C become
2 I overheard our teacher .... that she was going to give us a surprise test on Friday.
A saying B to say C say
3 If anyone is caught .... in the exam, they'll be sent home immediately and the paper discounted.
A cheating B to cheat C cheat
4 Can I persuade you .... me a hand with the household chores?
A giving B to give C give
5 In history class the teacher often lets us .... research on the computer for the projects.
A doing B to do C do
6 Jason reminded us .... to his place about seven o'clock to help him prepare the food for the party.
A going round B to go round C go round

3 Complete the sentences with the correct form of the verbs given. One sentence has more than one answer.

1 My parents have always encouraged me .... (try) new things.
2 Our teacher usually makes us .... (learn) ten new words a day.
3 I noticed Rachel .... (look) very sad today. Have you got any idea what's the matter?
4 We watched Sue .... (score) two amazing goals; she's great at football!
5 At the start of the year, the Spanish teacher recommended .... (listen) to some Spanish songs.
6 When I was younger, my parents only allowed me .... (stay up) later at the weekend.

4 Complete the sentences with the correct forms of the verb pairs.

advise/not visit • choose/receive • feel/shine find/walk • invite/go • let/use

1 I'm really pleased Mark .... us .... to his party last weekend because it was a fantastic evening.
2 It was a beautiful day and I could .... the sun .... on my face. It was really relaxing.
3 Our maths teacher .... us .... calculators in class, but not in exams.
4 They .... the missing boy .... in the woods. Luckily he was completely unharmed.
5 Recently the authorities .... all travellers .... the area until things have settled down again because it has become very dangerous.
6 The judges .... Malala .... the Nobel Peace Prize for all her work promoting education for children.

GRAMMAR CHALLENGE

5 Find and correct nine mistakes in the text.

I always found languages easy and been able to grasp even difficult structures without too much trouble. I enjoyed science, history and geography – but I would find maths very hard. Then I got a new teacher. She really encouraged me looking at maths in a different way. She made me understand many different aspects of maths that I had never been understanding before. She advised me do extra maths homework and when she noticed me struggling in class, she explained things again. Because of her, I started enjoy maths and I worked really hard. I was still really worried about passing my next exam, but I hadn't to worry because I got 75%! I didn't study maths at university, but she inspired me become a teacher, because I saw that a good teacher can really do a difference in someone's life.

Developing speaking

1 Tick (✓) the comments that are correct about giving a presentation.

1 Have a general idea of what you are going to say, then just start talking. You'll find ideas come to you as you go along. ☐

2 Make sure you put your ideas in order. That makes it easier for you and also for the listener to understand. ☐

3 Write out your presentation in full and then read it. That way you won't make any mistakes. ☐

4 Think about your presentation carefully beforehand and make notes to refer to. ☐

2 Look at the table with useful language for giving presentations. What should the last heading be?

Beginning your presentation	Ordering your arguments	Presenting opposing points of view	Responding to opposing points of view	....
To start with …	Firstly, … What's more, …	However, … You can't deny that …	But this does not mean that … Having said that …	To sum up …

3 Complete these phrases with the correct words and add them to the table in 2.

1 First of ....
2 You can't .... with the .... that …
3 I'd like to begin .... saying …
4 That doesn't .... my opinion that …
5 I would .... say that …
6 .... to my main point …
7 .... it's true that …

4 Read the article about a maths prodigy. Are you for or against home schooling? Why?

Fifteen-year-old Arran Fernandez is the youngest Cambridge student for over two hundred years! While most children of his age were just about to start school, five-year-old Arran sat and passed his maths GCSE (usually taken at age sixteen), setting a new record. He went on to take his 'A' levels several years early and is now going to Cambridge University to study one of the most difficult degree courses in the world – aged just 15. This young maths prodigy was home schooled by his father, who has rented a house in Cambridge to live in with his son. Arran plans to become a maths researcher.

5 LISTENING ▶ 07 **Listen to two presentations about home schooling and put the arguments in the order they are mentioned.**

a Home schooling is great because you avoid problems such as bullying.
b Home schooled children miss out on important aspects of school such as learning to mix socially.
c Home schooling might work for talented children, but it's not suitable for most children.
d Home schooling is perfect for talented children.

6 ▶ 07 **Complete the presentation with suitable words for each gap. Listen to Speaker 1 again and check.**

I'd **(a)** .... *to start by saying that I'm totally in favour of home schooling.* **(b)** ....*, it's perfect for talented children because it lets them progress at their own speed and this is very motivating. Secondly, it's beneficial for other children, too. There's no* **(c)** .... *that there's a lot of bullying in schools and* **(d)** .... *many children suffer from peer pressure. With home schooling, there is no bullying and no peer pressure. Let's not* **(e)** .... *that many less-gifted children struggle in school. Home schooling means they get continuous one-to-one teaching. In* **(f)** ....*, there are many reasons why home schooling is the ideal form of education.*

7 ▶ 07 **Listen to Speaker 2 again and circle the correct alternative.**

1 He *structures/doesn't structure* the presentation carefully.
2 He *uses/doesn't use* any useful expressions for giving a presentation.
3 He *presents/doesn't present* opposing points of view.

8 Make notes for a presentation arguing that home schooling is not the best form of education. Use ideas from Speaker 2, your own ideas and phrases from exercises 2 and 3.

1 Combine a prefix from A and a word from B to make words. Then use seven of them to complete the sentences.

A	B
co- • il • ~~im~~ • in inter • mis • over re • sub • un	cast • comprehensible conscious • legal • makes national • ~~penetrable~~ predictable • rated • starred

1 I must admit I'm not a fan of films with a plot that is ...impenetrable... I don't have the patience to work everything out and sometimes the producers make them simply ....!

2 In my opinion, films like the *Lord of the Rings* trilogy are extremely .... The special effects are good, but the acting isn't usually anything very special.

3 I like .... of old classic films because it brings good stories bang up to date for a new audience.

4 There are many films that are .... for under-16s to watch without a parent.

5 I like films that are .... I enjoy a real twist at the end!

6 Shailene Woodley .... with Theo James in the film *Insurgent*.

2 Circle the correct alternative.

1 Unfortunately the new film is rated 18 because it's too _cliché/risqué_.

2 The film *The Hunger Games* is _a sequel/ an adaptation_ of a book which I think works very well.

3 We all watched a thriller on TV last night. It was very _gripping/moving_.

4 Sometimes science-fiction films are a bit too _thought-provoking/far-fetched_ for my liking.

5 Ansel Elgort's _masterpiece/portrayal_ of a teenager in *The Fault in Our Stars* was excellent.

6 The latest *Star Wars* film will _deliver/hit_ our screens at the end of this month.

7 The musical *Wicked* received rave _receptions/reviews_ when it opened.

3 Read the review and complete the text with these words.

captivated • leading role • masterpiece • mesmerising performance • rave • recommend • special effects

I had some preconceptions about *The King's Speech*. I didn't believe that it could possibly live up to all the **(a)** .... reviews that surrounded its release. That, coupled with the fact that it won nearly every award going, was nearly enough to put me off going to see it – I rarely agree with the majority of critics. However, I am happy to say that I was proved wrong. In my opinion, it is quite simply a modern **(b)** .... The film stars a host of superb actors who give **(c)** .... performances. In the **(d)** .... we have the hugely talented Colin Firth who conveys perfectly King George VI's struggle to control a speech impediment. Supporting him as his speech therapist is Geoffrey Rush, who many may remember from his Oscar-winning performance in the film *Shine*. We are also treated to an excellent **(e)** .... by the multi-talented actress Helena Bonham Carter as Queen Elizabeth. All three main actors received awards, and deservedly so. The film centres on the speech problems of the reluctant King George VI and how he managed to overcome them. However, it is more than just a moving story about one man's struggle – it is about an unusual relationship between a monarch and a commoner and the development of trust between them. It also gives an enlightening picture of a particularly difficult time in history for the British monarchy. I was **(f)** .... by this film. For me, it is storytelling at its best without the expensive **(g)** .... that are so popular in today's film-making, and it is all about good acting. Additionally, it has raised the profile of an uncomfortable disability that is still misunderstood today, by portraying it in an accurate and sensitive manner. For once, I thoroughly agree with other critics and **(h)** .... *The King's Speech* to anyone who enjoys a good, old-fashioned, well-acted and superbly directed film. In my opinion this film has all the right ingredients to become a classic of the future.

4 Make notes about a film you have seen that you think will be a classic. Use the paragraph plan below.

Paragraph 1: General introduction and information.
Paragraph 2: More details about the film.
Paragraph 3: What you particularly liked about it.
Paragraph 4: Conclude by summarising and saying why you think it will be a classic.

5 Write your review using your notes as well as words and expressions from the Writing bank in the Student's Book.

Grammar

1 Circle the correct alternative.

1 Now Rob has got a better job, he can afford to buy/ buying a bigger house.
2 You've been getting headaches for a while now. I think you should consider to see/seeing your doctor about them.
3 Unfortunately, Chris failed to get/getting through the first stage of the competition.
4 I'm going to carry on to work/working for another few hours to finish my assignment.
5 Jack seems to be/being happier these days. Has he got a new girlfriend?
6 Did you volunteer to have/having your memory tested? It's fascinating!

2 Complete the sentences with the correct form of these verbs.

catch/play • force/practise • hear/say
persuade/meet • recommend/listen to • tell/not touch

1 If you really want to learn a foreign language, I .... you .... songs.
2 I loved learning the piano when I was young, but I hated practising. Now I'm glad my parents .... me .... every day!
3 Sam got extra homework yesterday because the teacher .... him .... a game on his mobile in class.
4 Last week my little brother accidently deleted some documents from my computer. I .... him .... it ever again!
5 Did I .... you .... that you live near here? Can you give me directions to the station?
6 I didn't want to go out, but in the end my friends .... me .... them in town.

3 Find and correct the mistakes in the sentences. Two sentences are correct.

1 My grandfather stopped to work when he was 75!
....
2 I once tried to learn Japanese, but it was too difficult.
....
3 We didn't see Jan because she already left when we arrived.
....
4 The teacher reminded us all revising for the test.
....
5 Jack shouldn't have lied to everyone, it was wrong.
....
6 I didn't know the meaning of the word, so I looked up it in the dictionary.
....

Vocabulary

1 Complete the words in the sentences.

1 I'm a bit **b**.................... by the amount of choice we have for dessert!
2 What's your earliest memory? I can't **r**.................... anything before the age of four.
3 Isabel finds it easy to understand chemistry, she has a **g**.................... for it.
4 I'm lucky, I don't usually find it hard to **g**.................... new concepts.
5 I tried to meditate but I found it hard because my mind was always **w**.....................
6 I hate public speaking because I'm not **a**..................... I find it difficult to explain things.

2 Choose the correct answers.

1 I didn't understand the new grammar at first, but finally I caught ....
A in **B** on **C** through
2 Jane moved to France last year and started learning French. She's really .... quickly!
A picked it up **B** picked up it **C** picked up
3 Mark .... with the idea for our presentation. It's going to be great.
A came up **B** kept up **C** talked through
4 When I moved to my new school, I was worried I wouldn't .... there, but I soon made new friends.
A stand out **B** get on with **C** fit in
5 We finally .... on a solution for the problem.
A pieced **B** hit **C** caught
6 Jackie is really good at maths. She says the secret is to .... patterns in numbers.
A look down on **B** look for **C** look out

3 Complete the sentences by adding the correct prefix to the words given.

1 I know a lot of people love spray tanning, but for me it's too .... **natural**
2 Sheila's our .... We used to live together when we were students. **housemate**
3 I couldn't follow what was happening in the film. It was very .... **jointed**
4 I don't know why Tom is so angry. It was just a .... **understanding**
5 Don't .... Frieda's ability. She's really a very, very good player. **estimate**
6 That answer doesn't make sense at all. It's completely .... **logical**

4 Mad science

Reading

1a VOCABULARY Solve the clues and complete the crossword.

Across

2 An .... is a type of protein that is produced by animals and plant cells.

5 Males have one X and one Y ....

9 .... engineering happens when you add genes to a living thing.

10 Many diseases are now becoming .... to antibiotics. It is very worrying.

Down

1 In an epidemic, many people .... the same disease.

3 A leech is a type of .... It lives on animals and feeds on them.

4 Yellow fever is a .... disease in Brazil, you must be vaccinated against it if you go there.

6 Some foods have been genetically .... so their genetic structure is different.

7 There are over a hundred different .... of birds in this area.

8 Birds can .... a type of flu to humans.

1b Complete the news stories with the correct form of words from 1a.

Pet trouble

'It's important to check your pet's health and give preventative treatment for fleas and gastrointestinal **(a)** .... because infected animals can then **(b)** .... them to humans.' That's the message from Sam Stevens, a local vet, after several families **(c)** .... giardia (a gastrointestinal disease) from their pets. 'People forget that there are diseases that can be caught from other animals,' Stevens explained.

GM Foods a Danger?

More than 85% of the corn and soy sold in the US comes from seeds that have been **(d)** .... However, nobody is sure yet about the impact these foods could have on our health. To date, research of the potential effects has only been done on other **(e)** .... such as hamsters.

Scientists hopeful of breakthrough

Sickle Cell Anaemia is a serious inherited blood disorder. It is more **(f)** .... among people of African, Caribbean and Asian origin. It is caused by a gene mutation and scientists are hopeful that one day they will be able to cure it with **(g)** .... They are hopeful that this type of gene therapy will also allow them to prevent **(h)** .... disorders such as Fragile X syndrome, a genetic condition that affects cognitive development.

2 Read the title of the article on page 31 and choose what you think it is about, a or b? Read the article and check your answer.

a Scientists are developing a possible new method of treating genetic diseases.

b Scientists have been using artificial chromosomes to improve humans' abilities.

3 Read the article again. Choose from the paragraphs (A–F) the one which fits each gap (1–6).

4 CRITICAL THINKING

Are the following fact (F) or opinion (O)?

1 Many human diseases involve genes. F/O

2 Synthetic biology involves designing new genetic material and life forms. F/O

3 It is unethical for scientists to change human chromosomes. F/O

4 The team produced the first chromosome for yeast. F/O

5 Genetic modification is the most important work scientists are doing today. F/O

5 Match the underlined words with the definitions.

1 a method for achieving something ....

2 from a point where nothing has been done, so you have to do everything ....

3 changes in genes that causes them to become different from others of its type ....

4 having doubt about something that other people think is right or true ....

5 made from artificial materials ....

6 faults in someone or something ....

COULD A MOUSE SAVE YOUR LIFE?

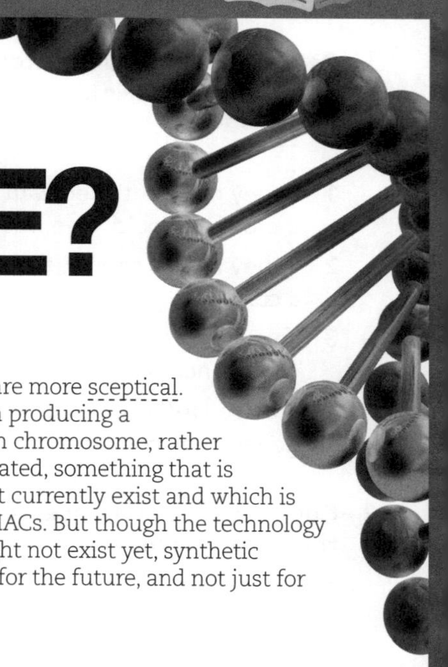

Scientists have created genetically engineered mice with artificial human chromosomes in every cell in their bodies in new gene therapy research that could save millions of lives. If you have a disease with a genetic cause, life can be incredibly difficult and, at present, most of these diseases do not have a cure. But now, it looks like these mice could be the answer and if this new research continues to be successful, there will eventually be a cure for all of them.

1 .... The new type of gene therapy, though, is far less risky and offers an exciting potential solution to the problem. Unlike genetic modification, this therapy, known as synthetic biology, involves creating entirely new, man-made genetic material like chromosomes, which are then added to cells.

2 .... The advantage of synthetic biology is that artificial chromosomes do not affect the other chromosomes in cells. This means that the artificial chromosome (known as 'chromosome 47' because the normal number of chromosomes in a human cell is 46) is much safer than conventional gene therapy. The implications for the treatment of disease are huge.

3 .... The researchers in the US and Japan working on the mice have so far been producing smaller versions of human chromosomes called HACs (human artificial chromosomes) from existing human chromosomes or creating them from scratch. If these HACs contained healthy versions of genes that are the cause of certain diseases, they could be used to cure people.

4 .... Others, however, are more sceptical. This new treatment would mean producing a synthetic version of a full human chromosome, rather than the mini versions so far created, something that is impossible using techniques that currently exist and which is far more complicated than the HACs. But though the technology for this type of gene therapy might not exist yet, synthetic biology is expected to be crucial for the future, and not just for genetic diseases.

5 .... Yeast is a favourite target for this type of research because it shares 2,000 genes with humans. The project aims to create all 16 chromosomes of the yeast fungus in order to develop entirely man-made yeast. Yeast is also a crucial component in the manufacture of food and biofuels so it has uses both in medicine and in other areas.

6 .... Producing and using artificial chromosomes either in yeast or directly in human cells has huge potential to save lives, but critics say that designing new forms of life has the danger of unexpected consequences unless more research is done. Some countries are refusing to invest in gene therapy using human chromosomes because they say it is unethical for scientists to create human life. As with many forms of cutting-edge science, the risks of using synthetic biology for humankind are unknown.

A The technology, though, is still very new and there is a long way to go before these cures can be used in humans. But there is clearly a lot of potential in this exciting new field of scientific exploration and many scientists are very excited about the possibilities for the future.

B The new artificial chromosomes could be used as a means of introducing new genes into human cells, meaning that any gene defects or DNA mutations in humans could be corrected. As these gene deficiencies are the cause of many diseases, this is a big breakthrough for medical science.

C Previously, it had been thought that a cure for genetic diseases lay in modifying existing human chromosomes. Scientists would alter the human genome (the complete set of genetic information for humans included in DNA) by adding an extra gene to an existing chromosome, often at random. If they had continued with this type of gene therapy, however, it would have been very risky since there is no way to predict how the gene might affect a human.

D The technique means that chromosomes, and therefore substances, can be given new properties that they don't normally possess. One company in California has already created a type of yeast that can produce artemisinin, an ingredient for an anti-malarial drug. Other research includes developing different synthetic genes for yeast so that it can produce a variety of antibiotics and vaccines.

E The research with genetically engineered mice is exciting progress in synthetic biology. Scientists were able to successfully introduce an extra human artificial chromosome in each of the mice's cells, the first time ever that a synthetic human chromosome had worked in an animal. And if a synthetic human chromosome works in a mouse, it could also work in a human.

F It could lead to important developments in many other areas, too. Agriculture and food production, the creation of antibiotics and vaccines and even the development of biofuels will all benefit from synthetic biology. The British government is investing more than £60 million in synthetic biology research, including £1 million on an international project to artificially construct a yeast fungus.

1 Read and match the sentences (1–4) with the type of conditional (a–d).

a Zero **b** First **c** Second **d** Third

1 If they had continued with this type of gene therapy, it would have been very risky. ……
2 If they are successful, there will eventually be a cure for all genetic diseases. ……
3 If you have a disease with a genetic cause, life can be incredibly difficult. ……
4 If these HACs contained healthy copies of genes, they could be used to cure people. ……

2 Complete the sentences with the correct form of the verbs given.

1 If space tourism …………………… (be) around when my grandad was alive, he'd definitely have gone on a flight.
2 It would be illegal if they …………………… (do) experiments on humans, so they are using rats.
3 If science lessons had been more interesting, I …………………… (concentrate) more when I was at school.
4 If the driving test …………………… (not be) so difficult, there would be more accidents on the roads.
5 If my brother …………………… (pass) his final exams, he'll be a doctor next month!
6 You are at risk of getting yellow fever if you …………………… (travel) to many parts of Africa.
7 They …………………… (make) a breakthrough sooner if a fire in the laboratory hadn't destroyed their experiments.
8 Scientists usually …………………… (get) more accurate results if they repeat experiments several times.

3 Correct the mistakes in the sentences. Some sentences have no mistakes.

1 I met Steve at a party. If I hadn't gone to the party, I would have met him!
2 If scientists eradicate malaria, far fewer people in Africa will die.
3 The researchers hope that if they are able to show the medicine works, the authorities would permit human trials to start.
4 They're short of money. If they had enough money, they will build a new hospital.
5 When these animals are young, you have to feed them every hour. If you didn't feed them, they die.
6 If I hadn't stayed up so late last night, I wouldn't have fallen asleep in class this morning.

4 Circle the correct alternative.

1 I'll write up the results this evening <u>in case/unless</u> I'm too tired.
2 <u>Supposing/Providing</u> we moved to the US, would the salary be similar there?
3 My parents let me go out during the week <u>as long as/suppose</u> I'm back by 9 pm.
4 I'll back up my work on the computer this afternoon <u>as long as/in case</u> it crashes again.
5 They'll give me the job <u>provided that/unless</u> they are happy with my references.

5 Choose the correct answers.

1 I wish I ………… more attention in class when I was at school.
A paid **B** had paid **C** would pay
2 ………… Peter wouldn't talk so loudly, it gets on my nerves!
A If **B** If only **C** Only if
3 I wish you ………… that! It's dangerous.
A didn't do **B** don't do **C** wouldn't do
4 I'm unemployed. I wish I ………… a job.
A had **B** had had **C** would have
5 Humans can't fly. If only we …………!
A flew **B** would fly **C** could fly
6 If only scientists ………… the answer.
A knew **B** had known **C** would know

GRAMMAR CHALLENGE

6 Complete the second sentence so that it has a similar meaning to the first sentence, using the word given. Do not change the word given.

1 I regret that I didn't score a goal in the football match yesterday. **wish**
I …………………… a goal in the football match yesterday.
2 I'll go to the cinema with you, but only if you promise to help me tomorrow. **that**
I'll go to the cinema with you …………………… to help me tomorrow.
3 When we were younger, we often watched my dad doing experiments. **would**
When we were younger, we …………………… experiments.
4 If the researchers don't find a solution, they will have to end the project. **unless**
……………………, they will have to end the project.
5 Jane won't watch science programmes that include animal experiments. **refuses**
Jane …………………… that include animal experiments.
6 I'd love to have some more money! **if**
…………………… some more money!

1 Put the letters in order in a–h and match them with words 1–8 to make compound nouns and adjectives. Are they written as one word (1), two words (2) or with a hyphen(-)?

1	genetically	a	horuhgt	....	☐
2	set	b	etmi	....	☐
3	life	c	psirgn	....	☐
4	world	d	cakb	....	☐
5	worth	e	irsk	....	☐
6	off	f	ofedidim	....	☐
7	break	g	hielw	....	☐
8	high	h	diwe	....	☐

2 Complete the sentences with compound nouns by adding prepositions to the verbs given.

1 The main .... (draw) to working in this lab is its size.

2 From the .... (set) the whole team has believed confidently in this project.

3 .... (cut) in public spending have meant that several research projects have lost their funding.

4 The .... (come) of the medical trials has been extremely successful.

5 The .... (break) of the disease affecting sheep has now been confined to a small area.

6 Our teacher always gives us useful .... (feed) on our homework.

7 Scientists have been working to find a cure for this problem and the .... (look) is good.

8 I'm afraid there has been a .... (break) in communications and we didn't receive your request.

3 LISTENING 08 Listen to an interview about the speed of human evolution. Which speaker, the presenter (P) or Jake (J), first mentions:

1 genetic Adam ....
2 the country where the study was done ....
3 genetic Eve ....
4 the first humans with blue eyes ....

4 08 Listen again and choose the correct answers.

1 Genetic Adam is ...
  a the most recent common male ancestor for men today.
  b a man who can trace his ancestors to an ancient human male.
  c the first human male ever to have existed.

2 In the Icelandic study the researchers ...
  a found that the men in the study had less than 174 paternal lines.
  b didn't find any genetic mutations in the men who participated.
  c studied over 750 men and grouped them by paternal line.

3 Researchers now know that genetic Adam ...
  a lived about 100,000 years ago.
  b lived at exactly the same time as genetic Eve.
  c probably lived around 250,000 years ago.

4 It is true that ...
  a only 7% of human genes have remained unchanged in human evolution.
  b a gene mutation led to humans having blue eyes and fair skin.
  c the gene for brown eyes is one of the more recent gene mutations.

5 Knowing about gene mutations and when genetic Adam lived ...
  a is something that has always fascinated the interviewer.
  b means scientists know more precisely when events in human genetic history happened.
  c can't yet tell scientists when humans first arrived in Europe.

VOCABULARY EXTENSION

5 Create nouns by adding the correct prepositions.

down • in • out • over

1 turn........: people who attend an event
2 ....come: the amount of money a person earns
3 take........: when one company buys another
4 ....turn: a decrease
5 ....burst: a sudden expression of emotion
6 ....take: the number of new students at a school or college
7 ....cry: a strong negative reaction to a decision by a large number of people

6 Complete the sentences with the correct compound nouns from 5.

1 The .... of students studying biology at this university has fallen this year.

2 There was a good .... at the lecture yesterday – they had to bring in extra chairs.

3 There's news of a .... of one of the big pharmaceutical companies.

4 I apologise for my .... this morning. I was really angry about the decision.

5 I'm looking for a new job as I want to increase my ....

6 There was an .... when the company decided to move its production overseas.

7 Due to the .... in the economy there will not be as much investment in research as last year.

1 Read the examples. Are they talking about an imaginary present situation (PRESENT) or an imaginary past situation (PAST)?

1 If scientists **had found** the information earlier, they **wouldn't be** researching it now. ....

2 If scientists **knew** exactly when Adam lived, they **would have been** able to pinpoint other historical dates. ....

2 Read the sentences in 1 again and circle the correct alternative to complete the rules.

1 To talk about an imaginary present situation and its *present/past* consequence we use:
If + past simple, ... *would/wouldn't have* + past participle.

2 To talk about an imaginary past situation and its *present/past* consequence we use:
If + past perfect, ... *would/wouldn't* + infinitive

3 Match the halves to make mixed conditional sentences.

1 I don't really like science fiction stories. If I liked science fiction stories, ...
2 I went to bed late. If I hadn't gone to bed late, ...
3 I don't need to speak French for my job. If I needed to speak it, ...
4 I missed the plane. If I hadn't missed the plane, ...
5 I'm good at maths. If I wasn't good at maths, ...
6 I had a lot of history homework. If I hadn't had any homework, ...

a I wouldn't be so tired now.
b I would be on holiday right now.
c I wouldn't know so much about King Henry VII.
d I would have read that book.
e I wouldn't have chosen to study it at university.
f I would have done a language course last year.

4 Complete the dialogues with the correct form of the verbs given.

1 **A:** Did you know the Golden Toad became extinct in 1989?
B: That's terrible! If we did more to protect reptiles like these, they .... (not become) extinct.

2 **A:** Why didn't you buy any chocolate?
B: I don't really like it. If I .... (like) chocolate, I would have bought some.

3 **A:** Do you want to go for a walk?
B: I can't. I have to work on my project. If I had finished my project, I .... (go) for a walk.

4 **A:** Why is the fridge empty?
B: I haven't been shopping. There would be food in the fridge if I .... (go) shopping.

5 **A:** Have you had lunch yet?
B: No. If I .... (have) lunch, I wouldn't be so hungry now!

6 **A:** Why didn't you come out with us last night?
B: I was tired. I would have gone out with you if I .... (not be) so tired.

GRAMMAR CHALLENGE

5 Find and correct the mistakes.

1 We won't be able to get home in case there is a train after 10 pm.
....

2 If you won't water plants, they die.
....

3 Sara persuaded us trying that new restaurant and we were glad we went.
....

4 Sam's face was red because he has been running for an hour.
....

5 I'd let you use my mobile if I brought it with me.
....

6 If I could travel anywhere in the world, I go to Cambodia.
....

7 Mike isn't here. I think he might go to the park to try out his new bike.
....

8 We only just missed the train. If we had walked more quickly, we would catch it.
....

9 Dominic admitted to take the money, but he denied stealing the watch.
....

10 If I hadn't lost my umbrella, I didn't be so wet now!
....

1 Read the texts about statistics and match the graphs (A–C) to the descriptions 1–3.

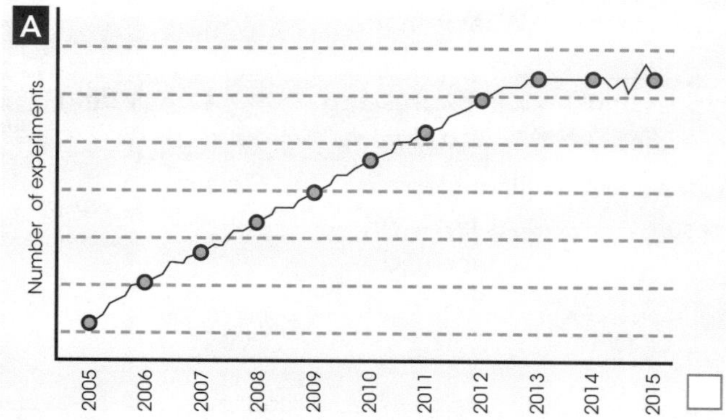

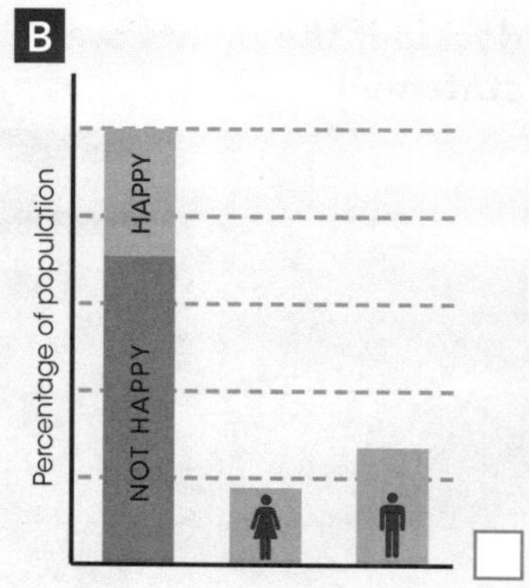

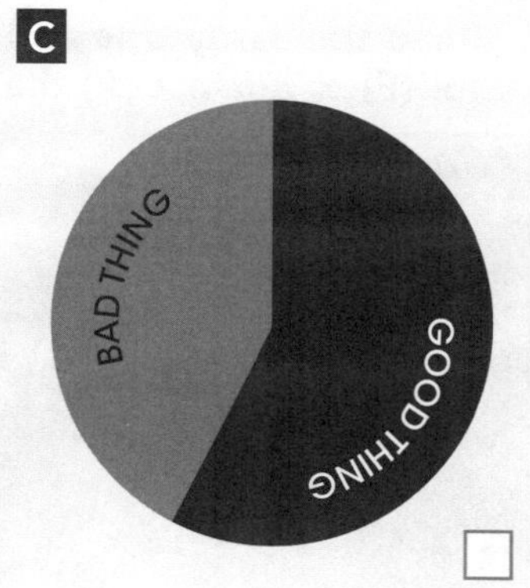

1 This bar chart shows that **(a)** .... (approximately) two thirds of the population are not happy about cloning animals. The interesting thing in my opinion is that there is a higher **(b)** .... (percentage) of women who are uncomfortable with it than men. Only 17% of women think it's OK, **(c)** .... (compared to) 27% of men.

2 In this pie chart you can see that just **(d)** .... (below) 60% of Americans think that work on cloning that helps with health problems is a good thing. However, just **(e)** .... (above) a third of the people surveyed don't agree with cloning.

3 You can see from the graph that the number of experiments **(f)** .... (increased) steadily between 2005 and 2013 and after that it **(g)** .... (stabilised). Between 2014 and 2015 it **(h)** .... (varied a lot).

2 Read the texts again and replace the words in brackets with alternative expressions with the same meaning.

3 Correct the following sentences.

1 One of four people strongly disagreed.

2 A quart of people questioned refused to give an answer.

3 Three times so many people made complaints this year compared to last year.

4 A considerable number of money was spent on advertising last year.

5 The third large response came from teenagers.

6 The number of research projects has fallen dramatic in the last two years.

7 The company's losses have levelled up in the last six months.

4 LISTENING 09 Listen to the results of a survey on climate change. Complete the charts and graph.

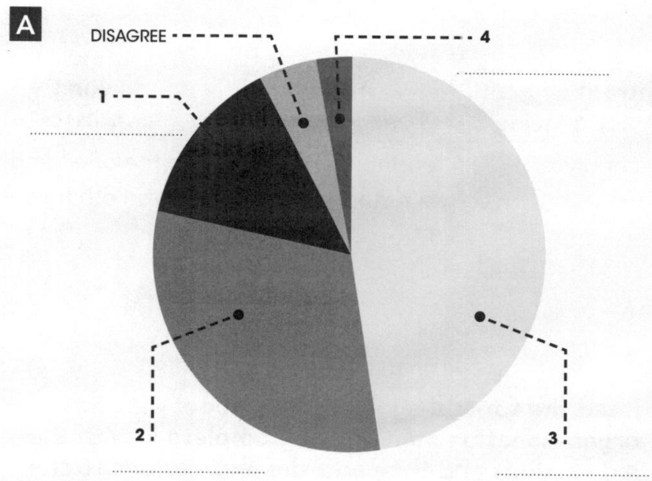

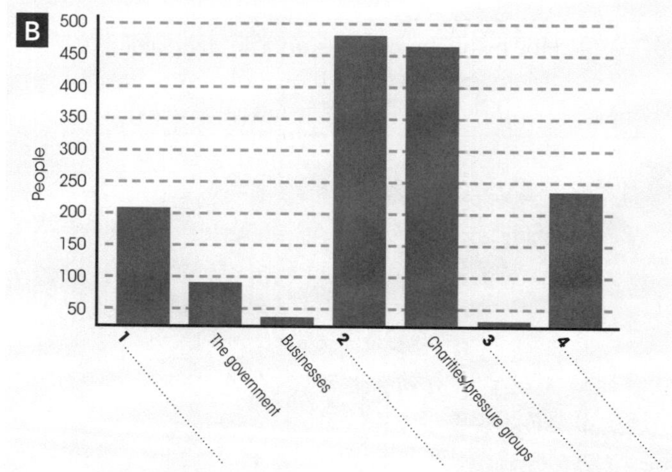

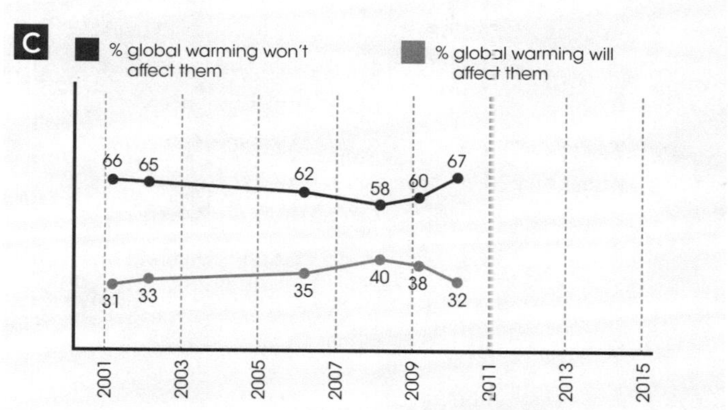

5 LISTENING 10 Complete the sentences about pie chart A with one word. Listen and check.

An overwhelming **(a)** .... said they agreed or strongly agreed that their actions were effective to help limit the effects of climate change – in fact, the **(b)** .... proportion, just under 50%, strongly agreed and about a **(c)** .... agreed. **(d)** .... under 20% said they neither agreed nor disagreed, and almost **(e)** .... in ten said they disagreed. A little **(f)** .... 5% said they strongly disagreed.

6 Write a paragraph to describe the other two diagrams in detail using words and expressions from the Speaking bank in the Student's Book.

1 Complete the table with these expressions.

All in all • Consequently • First and foremost • In contrast • In spite of • Last but not least
Moreover • Nevertheless • Personally, I believe that • What is more

Introducing and sequencing	Adding arguments	Making contrasts	Expressing consequences	Expressing opinions	Concluding
Secondly	Furthermore A further criticism of	On the one hand On the other hand	Therefore As a result	In my opinion As far as I'm concerned	To sum up

2 Read the for-and-against essay about making organ donation mandatory. Complete it with these expressions and then add the expressions to the table in 1.

However • In conclusion • In my opinion
Many people claim that • My own view
Others argue

The list of people waiting for organ transplants is reaching an all-time high with surgeons now able to transplant more and more parts of the body with increasing success. **(a)** ...., the number of organs donated for transplant is still a long way off meeting this demand and there have recently been calls for the UK to adopt a policy that is currently practised in many European countries. This is an 'opt-out' system where a person's organs would automatically be donated after death unless they had chosen to opt out while they were alive.

(b) .... a majority of people would willingly donate their organs but they do not get round to making this decision while they are alive. They believe that people must be encouraged to confront the decision and if they decide that they do not wish their organs to be transplanted, they can opt out of the scheme.

(c) .... is that this is a particularly difficult topic to deal with, as it is all about the rights of the individual. Some of those opposed to the move say it is all down to a matter of personal choice. **(d)** .... that it is not necessarily a lack of donor organs that is to blame for the problem, but a lack of facilities and qualified surgeons.

(e) ...., an opt-out system still allows for freedom of choice and I believe that it would be better to have an excess of possible donor organs than too few. **(f)** ...., I must say that I hope the debate over this crisis helps bring about a change in the law to make life easier and fairer for all those concerned.

3 Read the essay title and decide if the points are for (F) or against (A) the statement.

'Investing in space exploration is an expensive obsession we cannot afford.'

1 the money used for space exploration could be used to end poverty on Earth ....
2 space exploration brings huge opportunities for discovery and new scientific knowledge ....
3 through space exploration, we have the possibility of finding new places to live and new sources of important minerals and fuels ....
4 exploring space is very risky, people can easily die ....

4 Plan your essay. Use the ideas in 3 and/or your own ideas. Follow the paragraph plan below.

Paragraph 1: Introduction. Explain the situation
Paragraph 2: Present points FOR the statement
Paragraph 3: Present points AGAINST the statement
Paragraph 4: Summarise/personalise the points and make a conclusion

5 Write your essay using words and expressions from the Writing bank in the Student's Book and the checklist below.

Remember to check that:

- your paragraphs are well balanced
- your sentences are neither too long nor too short and are easy to follow
- you have used conditionals correctly

Grammar

1 Rewrite the sentences so the meaning is the same.

1 I might be free this evening. In that case I'll come to the science lecture with you.

If ....

2 I overslept this morning and missed my bus.

If ....

3 I didn't read about the experiment so I couldn't answer the teacher's questions in class.

If ....

4 My advice to you is to use a memory technique to memorise the new words.

If ....

5 I can't speak two languages so I didn't apply for that job.

If ....

6 I spent too long on the computer last night and now my eyes are tired.

If ....

2 Complete the sentences with the correct words.

1 .... you feel like playing tennis later, text me.

2 As .... as everyone agrees, we'll start work on our presentation tomorrow.

3 I can remember ten numbers in a row .... I'm interrupted.

4 The party was awful. I .... I hadn't gone to it – it would have been better to stay at home!

5 .... that there's not too much traffic on the roads, we should get there by 4.30.

6 .... nobody comes to the party? We'll have a lot of sandwiches to eat!

7 I hate getting up so early. If .... I could stay in bed longer!

8 When he was a student he was .... missing lectures.

3 Circle the correct alternative.

1 I'd go/have gone to the mountains last weekend if I hadn't hurt my leg.

2 If I'd watched the film last night, I would know/would have known what it's about.

3 I would speak/would have spoken better French if I'd lived there longer.

4 If I could meet any famous person in the world, I would choose/would have chosen Jennifer Lawrence.

5 You should have taken your coat as it might have been/might be cold.

6 I told her to stop to talk/talking so much during the science lecture.

Vocabulary

1 Choose the correct answers.

1 Scientists have made a .... in finding the cure for the disease. They hope to eradicate it in the next few years.

A breakdown B breakthrough C outbreak

2 Unfortunately, efforts to find a solution to the problem suffered a .... yesterday.

A setback B drawback C feedback

3 We had to spend long hours doing the research, but it was .... in the end.

A lifetime B offspring C worthwhile

4 The authorities want to stop illegal animal experiments and there has been a big crack .... on doing it.

A back B down C out

5 The research team have refused to comment on the .... of their experiments.

A outset B outlook C outcome

6 Kieran has to go for check-ups at the hospital every three months because he is a .... patient.

A high-risk B lifetime C setback

2 Complete the compound nouns in the text with the correct form of these words. Some words are used more than once.

back • down • in • out

The government is meeting again today to discuss further ways of making **(a)** cut.................... to help the economy. From the **(b)** ....set economists have been divided over the best way forward and have complained that their **(c)** ....put has not been listened to. They insist that there are many **(d)** draw.................... to the government's current policy and many would prefer a harder **(e)** crack.................... on the banking system. Whatever the **(f)** ....come of these most recent meetings, the financial **(g)** ....look for the country seems uncertain.

3 Complete the words.

1 I'm sorry I'm late, I got caught in a terrible traffic j.................... .

2 Men have one X and one Y c.................... ....

3 Cholera is a water-borne disease. It is usually t.................... by water.

4 Tom won't mind l.................... you a hand, he's always happy to help.

5 Many mosquitoes are now r.................... .... to anti-malarial drugs, so researchers are trying to find a new treatment.

6 I don't eat food that has been g.................... modified because we don't know what the effects could be.

7 Humans are probably the most dangerous s.................... of animal on the planet!

8 Ruth usually g.................... new concepts easily, she's very bright.

Reading

1 Read the article about artificial meat. Six paragraphs have been removed from the article. Choose from the paragraphs (A–F) the one which fits each gap (1–6).

A The researchers believe cultured meat could help feed the growing world population while reducing the impact on the environment. According to the analysis by scientists from Oxford University and Amsterdam University, artificial meat grown this way would reduce greenhouse gases by up to 96% in comparison to raising animals.

B Tuomisto predicts that if more resources are put into the research, the first commercially lab-grown meat could be available within five years. The first samples are likely to be like mincemeat in texture, while producing steaks could take at least five years longer. 'We can demonstrate that it is possible, but it is expensive,' she said.

C Another benefit would be to help animal welfare and protect endangered species. If most of our meat was grown, there would be no need for factory farms. Conditions for animals could be drastically improved. Elsewhere, it could also stop illegal endangered species hunts by providing an alternative way to produce meat from these species.

D 'The environmental impacts of cultured meat could be substantially lower than those of meat produced in the conventional way,' said Hanna Tuomisto, the researcher at Oxford University who led the study.

E The study found that growing meat in the lab rather than killing animals would generate only a tiny fraction of the greenhouse gas emissions associated with conventional livestock production. To produce artificial meat, or cultured meat as it is also called, involves extracting cells from an animal and converting them to muscle cells. The cells are then cultured with nutrients and essential vitamins and can be grown to any quantity and then shaped into hamburgers, steaks or mince.

F Aside from its predicted environmental benefits, cultured meat should also provide cheap nutrition. Animal protein is an increasing part of diets, as millions of people in rapidly emerging economies are drawn out of poverty and become able to afford more meat in their diets.

14th January

'Artificial meat could slice emissions and feed the world', scientists say

Meat grown artificially in labs could be a greener alternative for consumers who cannot bear to go vegetarian but want to cut the environmental impact of their food, according to new research.

1 ....

This may sound like science-fiction, but if you look at the shelves of any supermarket, you'll find 'engineered' products from soya meat to genetically modified fruit and vegetables. Artificial meat is not such a strange idea, and there are many good reasons for doing it.

2 ....

The process would require between 7% and 45% less energy than the same volume of conventionally produced meat such as pork, beef or lamb, and could be engineered to use only 1% of the land and 4% of the water associated with conventional meat.

3 ....

Tuomisto's research shows that cultured meat could be part of the solution to feeding the world's growing population, at the same time cutting emissions and saving both energy and water. Simply put, cultured meat is potentially a much more efficient and environmentally friendly way of putting meat on the table.

4 ....

The pressure this creates has been an important factor in rapidly rising grain prices, deforestation in the Amazon basin, increasing water scarcity and rising pressure to find new farmland. Growing meat artificially could potentially take huge pressure off farmlands around the world.

5 ....

So what does the meat taste like? Does the taste vary depending on the cells used? Nobody knows yet as humans are not allowed to eat it at present. However, the way cultured meat is grown means theoretically it could be produced to suit any consumer preferences – without any fat, with healthy fat, softer, with more muscle and so on. The possibilities are very exciting, but further research needs to be done before it is approved for human consumption.

6 ....

Exactly how long it takes before the meat is sold in supermarkets depends on the investment in research and development. Surprisingly, despite all its advantages, very few researchers are currently working on developing the cultured meat technology. Given that it could help to solve both our environmental crisis and the problem of how to feed the world, it is surely a goal worth working towards.

Use of English

2 Complete the second sentence so that it has a similar meaning to the first sentence. Do not change the word given. You must use between three and six words, including the word given.

1 Unless we practise harder, we won't win the competition. **if**

...., we won't win the competition.

2 Katie succeeded in finishing her project on time. **managed**

Katie .... on time.

3 You can go to the party, but only if you promise to be home by midnight. **that**

You can go to the party, ... to be home by midnight.

4 Gemma started playing that game three hours ago and she's still playing! **for**

Gemma .... three hours.

5 When I was a child, we often went to Spain on holiday. **to**

When I was a child, ... to Spain on holiday.

6 I'm absolutely certain that it was Oliver that I saw at the sports centre. **have**

It .... Oliver that I saw at the sports centre.

7 I'll talk to Ben and request that he book a restaurant for tonight. **ask**

I .... a restaurant for tonight.

8 I went out last night and didn't finish my project, so I can't go out tonight. **able**

If I'd finished my project last night, I .... go out tonight.

Listening

3 LISTENING 11 Listen to five people talking about how computer games affect the mind. Match the speakers (1–5) to the opinions (A–H). There are three extra letters which you do not need to use.

A There is a definite link between gaming and violent behaviour. ....

B All surgeons now have to play computer games to improve their abilities. ....

C Gaming has a beneficial effect on people's job performance. ....

D Computer games can help adults improve their memories. ....

E People worry about gaming when they should be considering bad effects of other things. ....

F Too many young people are addicted to computer games. ....

G Playing computer games has a negative impact on young people's learning. ....

H Computer games can help you develop a variety of useful skills. ....

4 11 Match the speakers (1–5) to the jobs (A–H). There are three extra letters which you do not need to use. Listen again if necessary.

A doctor ....

B business person ....

C lawyer ....

D teacher ....

E police officer ....

F student ....

G professional sportsperson ....

H journalist ....

Writing

5 Choose one of these two writing tasks. Write between 120 and 180 words.

1 Write an essay on the following topic using the notes below and/or your own ideas.

Some people think that genetically modified (GM) food is acceptable because it could help feed people in the future. Others think that it could have terrible consequences and put people's lives in danger.

Advantages: Good for the environment; Could solve world food crisis; Humane; Good for animal welfare

Disadvantages: Nobody knows the consequences; Still very expensive; Need strict controls

2 Write a review for this advertisement on a website.

FILM REVIEWS WANTED!

Have you seen a film that really made you think? Write a review of the film explaining why it made you think. Tell us whether you would recommend it or not. The best review will win a prize of £50.

COMMON MISTAKES

6 Correct the mistakes in the sentences.

1 If you want to relax I you recommend doing yoga.

2 The scientists are positive that if they do more research, they would find a solution.

3 I hope the teacher doesn't catch me do my homework in class.

4 As long that Jack goes to the party, I will go too.

5 Tom continued talk although the teacher had asked him to stop.

6 There's no deny that the weather is worse here than in southern Europe.

7 Why did Jane tell Peter to come? She shouldn't do that.

8 Sam's lost his car keys – if he hadn't lost them, he doesn't need to phone his wife.

9 In spite the fact that we discussed doing more research, nothing has happened.

10 I was having problems – Sara agreed to help me, but Tina refused helping me.

11 If you have arrived earlier, you would have met Pete, but he's already gone.

12 When I'm listening to long explanations, my mind tends wandering.

5 Big brother

Reading

1a VOCABULARY Read the clues and complete the puzzle to find the missing word.

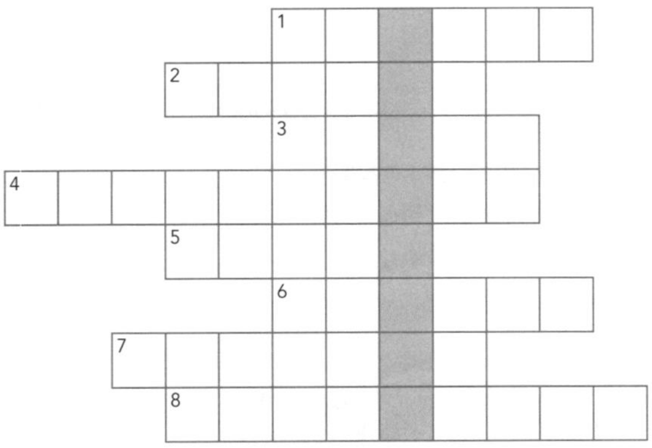

1 I was .... with a parking ticket for double parking.
2 The case will be .... in court next month.
3 The local council are introducing heavy .... for some offences.
4 You can't park there, it's a .... space for people with disabilities.
5 We are going to .... a complaint about the noise.
6 They were .... from the park after bad behaviour so they can't go there again.
7 They aren't sending him to prison, he has to do 100 hours of community .... instead.
8 .... is dropping rubbish in the street.

1b Complete the email with the correct words.

Hi Brian,

You know we moved to Sandstone Street last year? Well, I think we'll be moving again soon! There's a lot of rubbish in the road, but people don't use the bins despite the fact there's a sign up saying that anyone found **(a)** l.................... will be **(b)** i.................... with a **(c)** f.................... People don't take any notice, so I think they should make it a **(d)** h.................... one. Dad's getting really angry about the parking too – other people often park in places specially **(e)** d.................... for homeowners and it's a nightmare to find a space anywhere near the house now. Dad's **(f)** l.................... several **(g)** f.................... complaints, but there's no real action the authorities can take. To top it all, one of our neighbours was in **(h)** c...................., where he was **(i)** p.................... for stealing cars. Unbelievably, he was given a **(j)** s.................... sentence. He has to do some **(k)** c.................... service, but I suppose at least he'll have a **(l)** c.................... record.

All the best, Eve

2 Read the three articles (A–C) on page 41 about minor offences. Which article or articles involved:

1 school rules ....
2 a vehicle of some kind ....
3 a teenager ....
4 a family with young children ....
5 a possible court case ....

3 Read the articles again. Are the statements True (T), False (F) or is the information Not Mentioned (NM)?

1 Corey's driving was dangerous for other drivers. T / F / NM
2 Corey was given a warning before he was fined. T / F / NM
3 Other people in the town where Corey lives are concerned they could be fined for a similar offence. T / F / NM
4 Kathryn doesn't have enough money to pay the fines. T / F / NM
5 She feels her family has been discriminated against for having children. T / F / NM
6 The Mackenzies want to sell their home. T / F / NM
7 Savannah Keesee's mother agrees with the school principal about her daughter's hair colour. T / F / NM
8 Savannah has now dyed her hair back to its natural colour. T / F / NM

4 CRITICAL THINKING

How serious would you say the offences in the stories are? What sort of punishment do you think should have been given, if any?

5 Match the underlined words with the definitions.

1 do something that a law or rule does not allow, or break a law or rule ....
2 did something that is in opposition to a law, agreement, principle or rule ....
3 official warnings about disobedience or failure to cooperate ....
4 lose colour or brightness gradually ....
5 the reporting of an event by television, radio or newspapers ....
6 continued in a determined or unreasonable way ....
7 too much ....

It is illegal to ride lawnmowers on the road in Australia.

A

LAWNMOWER RIDING CRACKDOWN

A teenage boy in Australia owes $1,500 in fines after riding his lawnmower on a roadway. Police say they acted as they believe the teenager posed a threat to other road users.

Fourteen-year-old Corey Snowden from Stanford was hit with the fines last month after taking the lawnmower to the mechanic for repairs. As he was riding home, a policeman pulled him over, informed him he was breaking the law and took him to the police station. Corey then received two infringement notices for driving an unregistered vehicle and driving while unlicensed.

Corey's mother, Rebecca, believes her son should have been given a warning first. 'He's been driving the lawnmower to the mechanic for years and had no idea it was illegal.' She plans to fight the case and is going to take it to court, hoping to get the fines reversed. The court hearing takes place next month.

The incident, which has attracted national media coverage, has shaken the 2,000-strong community since many people ride their mowers on the roads to cut grass in their fields on the far side of the town near the railway station. They fear that if the Snowdens' court appeal fails, other people could soon be fined, too.

'It's left a lot of people worried about what's going to happen to them next,' Rebecca said.

B

STUDENT BANNED FOR 'TOO BRIGHT' HAIR

Many schools in the US do not allow students to dye their hair.

A high-school student was suspended from school for dying her hair 'a deep ultra-intense red'.

When Savannah Keesee returned to school earlier in March after a few snow days, she did not expect to be sent home for her hair colour. Savannah had dyed her naturally red hair a deeper shade of auburn during the break from school. She was standing in the lunch queue when West County High School's principal approached her and told her her hair colour violated the school's rules. He asked her to call her mum to come and pick her up. Savannah was sent home again the following day and banned from school.

The school rules state that 'non-natural colours will not be permitted. For example, green, purple, blue, etc.', but Savannah's mum insists, 'I dyed it auburn … and auburn to me is natural, just like strawberry blonde, blonde or dark hair.'

She believes the school should be worrying about more serious issues. 'Instead of maybe picking up on the bullying, and the kids who are actually causing trouble, it's hair colour,' she said.

The school principal, Stacy Stevens, said the hair colour policy had been in place for many years. 'We try to work with the students to be fair. We don't want them out of school. I think our students and parents are accepting of it. It's been in place a long time, and I think it's a policy that works.'

Savannah did not agree with the school ban and was refusing to dye her hair back to its natural colour as a matter of principle, arguing that it is a natural colour which will fade with time. She was planning to take the matter before the school board.

Since then the issue has been resolved and Savannah is returning to school next week as the ban will be lifted.

C

FAMILY FINED FOR 'NOISY' CHILDREN

Kathryn Mackenzie of Abbotsford says she and her family are being forced to leave their townhouse after being fined because her children play too loudly.

Kathryn, who lives with her husband and two sons, Gabriel, 2, and Jacob, 5, on the upper floor of a wood-framed house, has now received two fines for excessive noise.

The noise complaints were made by their downstairs neighbour, starting a year ago. The neighbour says that the children spend all day running and jumping and the noise is affecting her life. She claims the noise can be heard two floors down in the basement, despite the fact that the Mackenzie's apartment is carpeted throughout.

Kathryn is shocked that they have been fined for the children making noise in a strata complex (a type of apartment block with areas you share with other residents) that is considered to be 'family friendly'. The complex has a council of elected homeowners which can issue fines for any behaviour they consider to contravene regulations. Kathryn received the first $50 fine in November and the second a month later, together with a final warning threatening further action if the noise persisted.

'If it doesn't stop, we're going to be fined $50 every week,' said Kathryn. She has bought a foam mattress for the boys to play on and written to the strata council asking what they would like her to do to keep the children quiet, but has had no response.

Kathryn feels the council are making an unreasonable demand. 'I have to put this virtual stranger's comfort before the well-being of my children,' she said. 'I have been, in my opinion, bullied by my strata council because I have children.'

The Mackenzies fear the dispute will end in court and they have put their apartment up for sale. 'We can't afford to pay a family noise fee just to live in our home,' Kathryn said. 'We just need to get out now and I'll never buy in a strata complex again.'

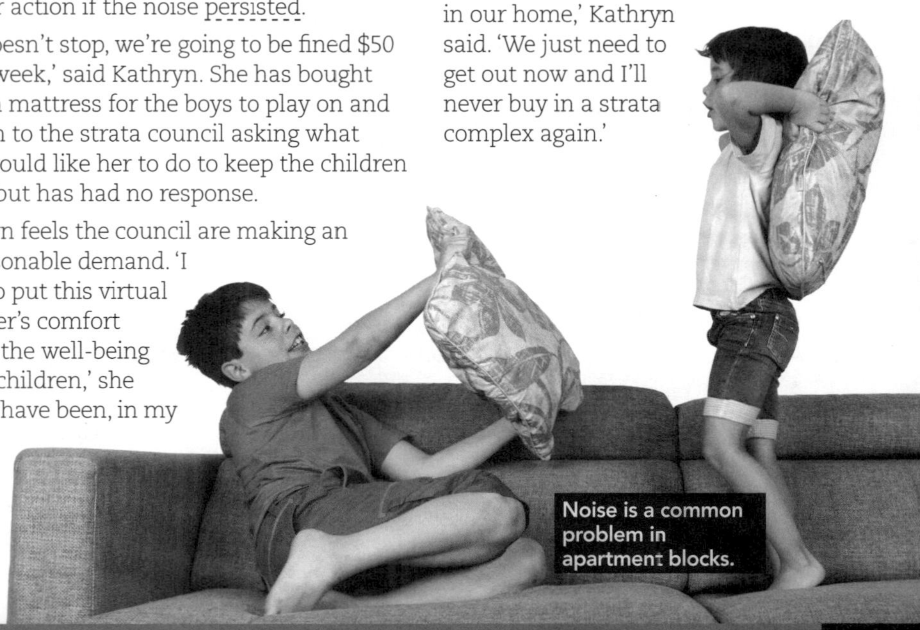

Noise is a common problem in apartment blocks.

1 Match the verbs in bold in sentences 1–6 with the uses (a–f).

1 She plans to fight the case and **is going to take** it to court. ....
2 The court hearing **takes place** next month. ....
3 The incident has left a lot of people worried about what**'s going to happen** to them next. ....
4 I**'ll never buy** in a strata complex again. ....
5 The Mackenzies fear the dispute **will end** in court. ....
6 Savannah **is returning** to school next week. ....

a to make predictions based on our opinions
b for general plans and intentions
c for fixed arrangements
d to make decisions about the future at the time of speaking
e for schedules and timetables
f to make predictions based on present evidence

2 Circle the best alternative.

1 I forgot to give Alfie the message, but don't worry, I*'ll phone/'m phoning* him now.
2 Alana's busy this afternoon. She *is going to/will* visit her cousins.
3 The next bus to London *leaves/is going to leave* at 4.10.
4 Maddox will be at the cinema in ten minutes. He*'s going to/will* leave home now.
5 Look out! That cup of coffee *is going to/will* fall!
6 We *will go/are going* to the park on Saturday afternoon. Do you want to come?

3 Complete the text with the correct option, A or B.

Authorities in New York have just announced plans for a new programme to deal with teenage crime. They expect that first-time offenders arrested for minor offences **(1)** .... to court, instead they **(2)** .... go to counselling sessions and do community service. The programme **(3)** .... on 1st February. Officials believe it **(4)** .... the number of low-level offenders that are slowing down the courts. Fourteen-year-old Jesse Jackson, who was arrested for riding the subway without a ticket, **(5)** .... one of the first people who benefit from the programme. 'I was offered the chance to go on the programme and when I accepted, they arranged a session for me. I **(6)** .... a counsellor next week. I think it's a great idea,' Jesse said.
Officials **(7)** .... the results of the programme in six months and decide whether to continue it or not.

	A	B
1	won't go	are not going
2	are having to	will have to
3	starting	starts
4	will reduce	is reducing
5	is going to be	is being
6	will see	am seeing
7	are going to review	are now reviewing

4 Complete the sentences with the correct form of the verbs in the box. Sometimes more than one answer is possible.

do • drive • go • like • open • snow

1 Do you know what time the shop .... tomorrow morning?
2 Look at the sky! I think it .... soon.
3 What .... you .... to celebrate your birthday?
4 I .... to the dentist tomorrow. I made the appointment ages ago.
5 My parents are meeting my best friend next weekend. I think they .... him.
6 We haven't got any bread. I .... to the supermarket and get some now.

GRAMMAR CHALLENGE

5 Choose the correct answers.

1 The trip included .... some fantastic sights in the city.
A visit B visiting C to visit
2 I .... go out, so I couldn't help my sister with her homework.
A should B must C had to
3 Janine .... upset if we don't go to her party tomorrow.
A gets B will get C is getting
4 Are you thirsty? I .... you a cup of tea in a minute.
A will make B am making C make
5 Turn off the gas on the cooker before you ....
A leave B will leave C are leaving
6 Mark .... him with his science project so we could learn more about it.
A let us helping B let us help C let us to help
7 We bought tickets for the concert last week. We .... tomorrow night!
A will go B are going to go C are going
8 The school holidays .... on Thursday 29th June.
A start B will start C are going to start
9 Joe .... to the park because he plays football there at this time every week.
A can't have gone B must have gone C might have gone
10 Sara was tired because she .... hard since 8 am that morning.
A has been working B was working C had been working

1 Complete the phrases with the correct prepositions.

1 Len was elected as mayor mainly .... account .... the policies he wants to introduce.
2 The police are prosecuting the man .... the strength .... the witness statements.
3 We're organising a festival to raise money .... aid .... refugees from Syria.
4 We're .... the process .... counting the votes in yesterday's election.
5 .... behalf .... the committee, Mr Brown thanked everyone who had helped at the event.
6 I think many politicians are .... of touch .... the needs of poor people.
7 The government is hoping to raise money .... means .... increased taxes.
8 .... addition .... reducing the number of subjects, the university is increasing its fees.

2 Use the prepositional phrases from 1 to complete the text.

I'm speaking not only for myself, but also **(a)** .... *everyone involved in my campaign when I say thank you for electing me mayor. Obviously the council is still* **(b)** .... *developing policies for the coming year, but* **(c)** .... *the public outcry about insufficient policing, we have already started recruiting.* **(d)** .... *increased numbers of police, we will also be investing in more CCTV cameras for the city centre. We believe past councils have been* **(e)** .... *how the public feels on many issues, so we plan to rectify this* **(f)** .... *a series of surveys. I would like to close by saying that our local schools will be organising a series of entertainment events* **(g)** .... *local charities – please book you tickets early* **(h)** .... *limited seating availability. Once again, thank you all for voting.*

3 LISTENING 12 Listen to a report about new technology being used to fight crime. Match the technology (1–5) to the explanations (a–e).

1 Brain fingerprinting ....
2 PredPol ....
3 SmartWater ....
4 DeltaSphere-3000 ....
5 OnStar ....

a is used to recreate 3D images of crime scenes
b can see when suspects are lying
c can be used to slow cars down
d is being used to predict where crimes might happen
e can be sprayed on items so they can be identified

4 12 Listen again and answer the questions with a maximum of four words or numbers for each one.

1 What two indicators do traditional lie detectors use?
....
2 What does brain fingerprinting see inside a brain?
....
3 How accurate do scientists think brain fingerprinting will be? ....
4 What times and locations does PredPol base its predictions on? ....
5 By what percentage have burglaries fallen since they started using it? ....
6 What does SmartWater contain to identify possessions?
....
7 Where are the 3D images of crime scenes also being used, apart from in solving crimes?
....
8 What are police in Japan using 3D technology for?
....
9 After OnStar has been activated, what speed can a car travel at? ....

VOCABULARY EXTENSION

5 Complete the sentences with these phrases.

at the sight of • for the attention of
for the purpose of • in exchange for
in fear of • in need of

1 Many people worldwide live .... intolerant political regimes.
2 I feel sick .... blood.
3 This report is .... the manager.
4 The judge gave him a reduced sentence .... information leading to other arrests.
5 I have called this meeting .... discussing a new strategy.
6 We are .... a babysitter for tonight.

1 Look at the sentences and complete the rules with these words.

future continuous • future perfect continuous
future perfect simple • going to happen very soon

1 We use the .... to talk about an activity in progress at a moment in the future. E.g.
*Police here **will** soon **be using** a system called brain fingerprinting.*
2 We use *be on the verge of/be on the point of* to talk about things that are .... E.g.
*They're **on the point of using** it more widely around the country.*
3 We use the .... to talk about an activity completed before a specific time in the future. E.g.
*They **will have installed** all the microphones by the end of the month.*
4 We use the .... to emphasise the duration of an activity that continues up to a particular time in the future. E.g.
*Police **will have been using** it for only six months, but they expect the results to be very promising.*

2 Choose the correct answers.

1 This time tomorrow I .... on the beach!
A will be lying B am on the verge of lying
2 We're moving to Canada soon. We .... there next month.
A will be living B are on the point of living
3 The train leaves in one minute. It ....
A will be leaving B is on the point of leaving
4 Scientists .... that problem – it won't be long before they have a solution.
A will be solving B are on the verge of solving
5 What .... in the holidays? Have you got any plans?
A will you be doing B are you on the verge of doing

3 Complete the sentences with the future perfect simple or the future perfect continuous form of the verbs given.

1 I'm making cakes now. I .... (finish) in five minutes.
2 Jackie is very ambitious. She's only just started her company, but she's sure she .... (create) a successful business in less than five years.
3 Jake first played tennis when he was five. By this time next year, he .... (play) for ten years.
4 I'm sure I .... (buy) a house or a flat by the time I'm thirty.
5 At the end of this year, I .... (study) Spanish for six years.
6 Let's stop soon. We .... (drive) for four hours by the time we reach the next town!

4 Complete the text with the correct future form of these verbs.

be • get (x2) • have • send • sign • sit
talk • travel • work

I'm at the airport now. By the time you get this message, I **(a)** .... for at least four hours! I still can't believe that at this time tomorrow I **(b)** .... in a meeting in New York. I didn't plan to be going there so soon! However, the American company is on the verge of **(c)** .... an agreement with us, so I'm sure that when we **(d)** .... the contract (and I'm sure that we **(e)** .... it!), it **(f)** .... worth all the effort. I imagine that Mark **(g)** .... you all the details about the new commission by now, so you **(h)** .... on that from Monday through to Thursday. Anyway, I **(i)** .... to you when I'm back in the UK in case you **(j)** .... any problems.

GRAMMAR CHALLENGE

5 Complete the second sentence so that it has a similar meaning to the first sentence. Do not change the word given. You must use between three and six words, including the word given.

1 I started work at 9 o'clock and it's almost 12 o'clock. **will**
By 12 o'clock I .... for three hours.
2 My meeting starts at 3 pm tomorrow. **sitting**
I .... in a meeting at 3.10 pm tomorrow.
3 It would be fantastic to win the competition. **only**
.... the competition!
4 'You should ask your teacher for help,' John said to her. **advised**
John .... her teacher for help.
5 Sam is going to ask Susan to marry him very soon. **verge**
Sam .... Susan to marry him.
6 It wasn't a good idea for me to lie. **should**
I .... the truth.
7 I've almost finished my homework. I'll finish by 10 pm. **will**
By 10 pm I .... my homework.

1 LISTENING 13 **Listen to the dialogue. Are the sentences True (T) or False (F)?**

1 Kate wants to ask Max's advice about something. T/F
2 Kate suggests downloading some songs in English. T/F
3 Max finds it easy to understand song lyrics in English. T/F
4 Max asks Kate to clarify what she means about watching films. T/F
5 Max doesn't think Kate's suggestion is very sensible. T/F

2 13 **Complete the sentences from the dialogue with suitable phrases. Listen again and check.**

1 You like music, so .... downloading some songs in English?
2 ...., I don't always understand what they're saying.
3 There are some great websites with song lyrics – .... check them out?
4 .... idea. .... try to learn the lyrics?
5 Watching films is good too – .... that?
6 .... films in English?
7 .... sensible.

3 **Complete the phrases in the table with these words. Then add the phrases from 2.**

about • better • ideal • might • saying • think • were • what • would (x2)

Asking for advice	Giving advice	Responding to advice/Asking for clarification
If you .... me, would you …? What do you .... I should …? What .... …?	You .... want to … If I were you, I .... … You ought to/had .... …	That sounds helpful/.................... But .... about …? Don't you think it .... be better to …? Are you .... that …?

4 **Use phrases from the table to complete the rest of the dialogue. Sometimes more than one phrase is possible.**

Max: I'm thinking about subscribing to a newspaper every week, too. Can you recommend one?

Kate: There's a good daily paper called *The Echo*. **(a)** .... try that and see how much you understand?

Max: Right. **(b)** .... read it all the way through?

Kate: **(c)** ...., I'd find the sections that interest you and read those, like sport and lifestyle.

Max: **(d)** .... **(e)** .... the headlines and news stories?

Kate: **(f)** .... avoid those until your language is better. And **(g)** .... getting English magazines? It might be easier and they always have interviews with celebrities and sports stars.

Max: **(h)** ....! **(i)** ...., I'm not sure I'll be able to buy them in my country.

Kate: Don't worry, I'll send you some.

5 **Read the exam task and make notes about the advice you would give.**

A British friend wants to visit a tourist destination in your country and needs advice. Discuss the following issues.
- which place to go and why
- accommodation
- safety in the area
- what to take with you

6 **Write the dialogue using your notes as well as words and expressions from the Speaking bank in the Student's Book.**

1 Rewrite the sentences replacing the words in bold with these expressions.

highly • merely • a number of • numerous
providing • the vast majority of

1 These cuts are **just** the beginning – there will be others.

....

2 There have been **some** complaints.

....

3 I demand that you concentrate on **offering** better services.

....

4 **Most** people disagree with the proposed cuts.

....

5 **Many** town councils have reduced administration costs.

....

6 It is **very** possible that the council will reduce police numbers.

....

2 Read the letter of complaint and complete it with the words from 1.

Dear Sir/Madam,

I am writing on behalf of the residents' association in Belmore to protest about your proposed cuts to our local services. I believe that these cuts would not only be unpopular, but would also significantly reduce the quality of life in Belmore.

Firstly, concerning the street lighting, I should like to draw your attention to that fact that **(a)** .... residents have active social lives which often entail us driving or walking through the streets at night time. The street lighting is essential for us to feel confident and safe.

My second complaint concerns the proposed cuts to the number of police on the streets in Belmore. It is a ridiculous idea since there are a worrying **(b)** .... street crimes every week. The fact is that reducing the number of police will **(c)** .... encourage street crime.

Your plan for fortnightly rubbish collection is also **(d)** .... impractical. Although it will reduce costs, it will mean bags and bins of rubbish littering the pavement. For this reason, I believe the measure will prove ineffective as it will take the dustbin men longer to clear the rubbish and mean the streets have to be cleaned, which is costly. To make matters worse, the increased bags of rubbish attract rats and this is a serious health hazard.

In conclusion, as you can imagine, I have received **(e)** .... letters and emails from local residents expressing their concerns and I would ask you to reconsider your proposals. Might I suggest that any cuts should be made in reducing the amount spent on council administration? I urge you to concentrate on **(f)** .... the best possible services for the neighbourhood, not making cuts that will make it a worse place to live.

Yours faithfully,

Maggie Ashdown

3 Read the letter again and find nine expressions from the Writing bank in the Student's Book.

4 Complete the table with the underlined words and phrases in the letter.

Contrast	Give reasons	Conclusion

5 Max is a student at Newtown Secondary School. Read the newspaper article and Max's notes and answer the questions.

1 How many reasons are given for closing the school?

2 Does Max make points against all the reasons?

SCHOOL TO CLOSE!

Mayor Daniel Blunt has announced today that Newtown Secondary School is to be closed. The decision has been taken because student numbers have fallen and standards at the school have also dropped. The school needs urgent repairs, which the council believes will be too costly. Students will be allocated to new schools. The news comes at a time when other closures

- *Lower numbers good – before was overcrowded*
- *Changing schools very bad for students – for education, increased travelling, etc.*
- *Standards excellent – look at exam results*
- *It's a wonderful school because: teachers, sports, spirit*
- *School is in bad condition because authorities refused to give money to help*

6 Plan a letter to the mayor. Organise Max's points into paragraphs and develop and add your own ideas.

Paragraph 1: Introduction
Paragraph 2: Main points
Paragraph 3: Additional points
Paragraph 4: Conclusion

7 Write your letter of complaint using expressions from the Writing bank in the Student's Book and the checklist below.

Remember to check:

- the organisation of your ideas
- use of formal language
- use of conjunctions (*although*, *since*, etc.)

Grammar

1 Read the sentences and decide what you would say in each case.

1 Your brother suggests watching a film this evening, but you are tired.
I'm sorry. I .... (go to bed).

2 A reporter asks you for your predictions about littering.
I think littering .... (get worse).

3 The washing machine is making a strange noise again.
Oh no! I'm sure it .... (break) soon.

4 It's early in the morning and you are waiting outside a shop. You don't know the opening time.
Excuse me. What time .... (open)?

5 A friend has invited you to a barbecue at his house on Saturday, but you are away at your grandparents' house.
I'm sorry. I .... (visit my grandparents).

6 Your friend is playing a computer game for the first time, but he isn't doing well.
I think you .... (lose).

7 Your little brother doesn't understand his homework.
Don't worry. I .... (help you).

2 Complete the sentences with the correct form of the verbs given.

1 Let's stop in the next village for lunch because we .... (walk) for three hours by then.

2 When I saw Mark he was on the verge of .... (give up) his job because he was so stressed.

3 We're celebrating Nick and Marie's wedding anniversary next Friday. They .... (be) married for five years by then!

4 At many job interviews they ask you what you think you .... (do) in five years' time.

5 I'm pretty sure the film .... (finish) by ten thirty, so I'll ring you then. OK?

3 Correct the mistakes in the sentences.

1 I moved here almost ten years ago – next month I will be living here for ten years.
....

2 I want finishing my book tonight, so I'm not going out.
....

3 What do you do at this time tomorrow?
....

4 Tom was very rude – he might not speak to the teacher like that.
....

5 What are your plans for the weekend? Do you do anything special?
....

6 We will finished eating by eight o'clock so I can meet you then.
....

Vocabulary

1 Write the words for the definitions.

1 a large amount of money as a punishment for not obeying a law or rule ....

2 dropping things like small papers or sweet wrappers in the street ....

3 time that someone will have to spend in prison only if they commit another crime within a fixed period of time ....

4 make an official complaint about something ....

5 officially accuse someone of a crime and ask a court to judge them ....

6 say officially that a place has a particular purpose ....

7 work that someone does as a punishment instead of going to prison ....

8 say officially that someone is not allowed to do something ....

2 Complete the sentences with *by*, *in* or *on*.

1 The council have decided to change their housing policy .... the strength of public reaction to their plans.

2 We're running a marathon on Saturday .... aid of a children's charity.

3 I got the right answer .... means of eliminating the impossible options.

4 My dad's .... the process of designing an extension to our house, but it won't be finished for another week.

5 The teacher wants us to write an essay .... addition to the exercises she's already given us for Friday.

6 .... behalf of the whole team, I'd like to congratulate you on the success of the project.

3 Complete the sentences.

1 Janet has been i........................ with a parking fine by a traffic policeman.

2 My mind often w........................ in lectures. I can't help thinking about other things.

3 The car had been in the sun for hours and the s........................ w........................ was really hot when I put my hands on it.

4 He was fined for smoking in a n........................-d........................ area. Smoking is not permitted there.

5 She's giving me the c........................ s........................ because she thinks I told everyone her secret, but I didn't. I hope she starts talking to me again soon.

6 I think g........................ e........................ is a dangerous thing – you shouldn't try to add genes to living things.

6 Moving home

Reading

1a VOCABULARY Find six words and expressions in the word search related to finding a place to live. Then complete the sentences.

1 We don't need to buy a sofa or bed or anything because the flat is ....
2 We're so excited! We found a house for rent that we love. We've just put down a ....
3 We've just bought a flat. The decoration is very old-fashioned so we're going to .... the whole flat. We start painting it tomorrow.
4 I've packed everything. I'm going to .... to my new place next week.
5 We can't stay in this house any longer. Let's .... this weekend – hopefully it won't take long to find a house we like!
6 My friend and I rent a flat together. It's a great .... because we each have our own bedroom and bathroom.

F	H	O	X	C	W	W	N	V	A	I	C
U	I	S	V	T	I	E	B	U	X	J	H
L	J	V	Z	E	O	N	A	R	C	F	N
L	W	A	N	G	E	Y	J	L	T	L	V
Y	Q	P	D	E	T	X	D	N	I	A	P
F	R	F	S	J	T	P	U	P	P	T	T
U	Z	H	M	O	D	H	R	Z	U	S	R
R	R	B	P	O	E	E	C	N	J	H	P
N	U	P	J	S	V	V	P	W	O	A	V
I	G	B	U	F	O	E	D	O	G	R	S
S	U	O	Y	I	L	K	I	F	S	E	H
H	H	M	Y	E	B	F	H	N	E	I	K
E	U	F	F	J	G	S	O	A	E	F	T
D	O	U	P	M	Y	U	H	J	A	G	K

1b Choose the correct answer.

1 I didn't have enough money for the rent, luckily my .... agreed to wait a week.
A lodger **B** landlady **C** tenant
2 Usually, you have to sign a contract for a flat or house before you can move ....
A in **B** into **C** up
3 The decoration in our house needs modernising. We're going to .... the kitchen first.
A do up **B** do down **C** do in
4 I've got a .... living in my house with me, we get on well.
A landlord **B** tenant **C** lodger
5 This flat is too small, I'm going to start .... for a bigger one.
A flat-sharing **B** flat-hunting **C** flat-looking

2 Read the articles quickly on page 49 and match the titles (1–4) with the articles (A–D).

1 Small is beautiful ....
2 Life under the waves ....
3 An independent lifestyle ....
4 From storage to homes ....

3 Read the articles again. For questions 1–10 choose from the articles (A–D). The texts can be chosen more than once.

Which article mentions somebody who ...
1 describes an improvement in their health since moving home? ....
2 talks about feeling satisfied at the achievement of creating a home? ....
3 uses the wind as a source of energy? ....
4 chose their home for ecological reasons? ....
5 thinks the price of the house is reasonable considering the views? ....
6 talks about being part of a community of like-minded people? ....
7 mentions having a different job as a result of moving home? ....
8 has a very expensive bathroom? ....
9 describes how the house is built? ....
10 built flats near a river to rent out? ....

4 CRITICAL THINKING

What do you think would be the advantages and disadvantages of living in one of these homes?

5 Match the underlined words to the definitions or explanations.

1 publically supports a particular policy or way of doing things ....
2 joined two pieces of metal together by heating them and pressing them together ....
3 provide something that is wanted or needed, often over a long period of time ....
4 causing little or no damage to the environment ....
5 attracted to, interested in ....
6 very successful ....
7 able to provide everything you need, especially food, without help ....

A

Most homes in the UK and around the world are connected to networks that supply electricity, gas, water and phone lines. But an increasing number of people are now going 'off the grid', creating their own energy and water supply.

Nobody knows exactly how many people live in off-grid homes in the UK, but most estimates put it at between 75,000 and 100,000 people. Some are drawn to the lifestyle for economic reasons. One homeowner, Jim Lynch, told us that he lived on a houseboat in London because he didn't want to pay any rent money to property developers or energy companies. He added that he was almost self-sufficient as he made his own diesel from vegetable oil.

For others, the motivation is living in a sustainable way and reducing their carbon footprint. Sasha and Iain Pocock have lived off-grid on a small farm for 19 years. They grow their own food as well as keeping animals. They get their electricity from a generator and a wind turbine.

Off-grid homeowners seem to agree that life off-grid isn't always easy, but it has many advantages, such as the slow pace of life and the security of never having to pay bills.

B

The Tiny House Movement is a social movement that advocates living in small homes. These can be permanent or temporary, off-grid or connected to an energy supply, in cities or in the countryside. But one thing they have in common is their size and the owners' desire for a simple lifestyle.

Tammy and Logan Strobel have lived in their tiny house since 2011. It's just 17 m^2, smaller than most parking spaces, and is on wheels in case they ever want to move. It cost them \$33,000 but they have no mortgage and their general household expenses come to only \$500 a month.

Tammy recommends living in a tiny house because having less space for possessions means that she spends less money on new things, allowing her to leave a job she didn't enjoy and do something she loved instead. She now writes online as well as volunteering.

Many people ask her if she misses her privacy, but Tammy insists that she and her husband get along really well. If she needs some personal space, Tammy goes for a walk. 'We want to spend our money on experiences rather than on things. I notice the seasons change and participate in the community more. Not to mention with biking, walking and eating right, I feel so much healthier.'

C

Shipping containers are usually used for transporting goods but now imaginative homeowners are proving that they can be great places to live. You might imagine that metal boxes would not make good living spaces, but you'd be wrong.

The boxes can be joined together to form larger spaces in unusual shapes and it's easy to put in windows and doors.

Farmer and architect Patrick Bradley created his perfect home out of four shipping containers, welded together in the form of a cross. The low cost of the containers compared to building a brick house, meant he could include a luxury bathroom with a £16,000 bath – and the total cost was only £133,000.

One architect took the idea one step further and created Container City, a four-storey high block of flats in London that is made entirely of shipping containers, overlooking the river. It's a thriving community of artists and musicians, with a restaurant and performance space, too. Becky McGahern rents a 40 m^2 flat there that doubles as her office. Becky says that she loves being part of this community. 'There are a lot of musicians, so in the evenings, people will get their violins out and I'll bring my face paints.'

D

People have dreamed of living under the sea for years, and now their dreams are close to becoming reality.

US Submarines Inc has created the world's first undersea residence called H2OME. L Bruce Jones, the president of the company, is proud of their achievement. 'It's circular in plan and about 20 m in diameter, but the most important thing is that the interior is at the same pressure as on land,' Jones says. This means you could easily live underwater and commute to work on land.

The H2OME has three bedrooms, three bathrooms, a kitchen, a dining room and a living room built around a central column which supplies the power and oxygen. The outer rooms have huge floor-to-ceiling windows. 'We manufacture in a dry dock and then the structures are floated out and sunk. We then build legs so that the structure stands above the sea floor,' Jones explains.

If you feel like buying one of these aquatic homes, you'll need to start saving as prices start at around \$10 million. One architect who worked on the project claimed that this isn't a lot of money for a house with a view onto a reef, but it seems that underwater living will remain only for the wealthy.

1 Read the examples and match the verbs in bold with some of the forms (1–8).

Jim Lynch **told** us that he lived on a houseboat in London.
He **added** that he was almost self-sufficient as he made his own diesel from vegetable oil.
Off-grid homeowners seem to **agree** that life off-grid isn't always easy.
Tammy **recommends** living in a tiny house.
Many people **ask** her if she misses her privacy.
One architect **claimed** that this isn't a lot of money for a house with a view onto a reef.

1 verb + (*that*) + sentence in reported speech with change of tense
....
2 verb + object + (*that*) + sentence in reported speech
....
3 verb + question word/*if* + sentence in reported speech
....
4 verb + (*not*) *to* infinitive
....
5 verb + object + (*not*) *to* infinitive
....
6 verb + gerund
....
7 verb + (object) + preposition + gerund
....
8 verb + (*that*) + object + (modal) + infinitive without *to*
....

2 Add these verbs to the correct sections (1–8) in 1.

accuse somebody of • agree • announce • apologise for • claim • complain • congratulate somebody on • criticise somebody for • demand • forbid • inform • instruct • invite • offer • recommend • regret • remind • suggest • want to know • warn • wonder

3 Circle the correct alternative.

1 Our teacher warned us *to be/of being* careful when using reporting verbs.
2 Tom suggested *to have/having* a party for my birthday.
3 Dad insisted *I cutting/that I should cut* the grass before going to the football match.
4 Lauren offered *to give me/me to give* a lift to the station after school.
5 Matt accused *that I had cheated/me of cheating* in the exam.
6 The estate agent advised us *not to wait/we didn't wait* too long before putting down a deposit on the house.
7 Our neighbours complained *of our playing/that we had been playing* music too loudly at night.

4 Complete the sentences with these words. Then rewrite the sentences in direct speech.

admitted • advised • asked • ~~congratulated~~ • recommended

1 Bella *congratulated* me on passing my driving test.
Well done on passing your driving test!
2 Yesterday a government official .... people not to travel to Kenya.
....
3 The thief .... stealing the money.
....
4 Kate .... that we should try the restaurant.
....
5 Steve .... if I had heard the news.
....

5 Complete the second sentence so it has a similar meaning to the first sentence. Do not change the word given. You must use between three and six words, including the word given.

1 'I won't increase the rent,' the landlord said. **agreed**
The landlord ....
2 'I wish I hadn't done it,' Jack said. **regretted**
Jack ....
3 'Is the flat available?' we asked. **wondered**
We ....
4 'We will win the election,' the politician said. **claimed**
The politician .... the election.
5 'I will definitely help you,' Jasper said to me. **promised**
Jasper ....
6 'It's not a good idea to move house now,' the estate agent said. **warned**
The estate agent .... house now.

GRAMMAR CHALLENGE

6 Correct the mistakes in the sentences.

1 Mark refused helping me to clean the flat.
....
2 We shouldn't do that, it was a terrible idea.
....
3 Neil offered go flat-hunting with me.
....
4 By the time I finish my project, I'll be writing 5,000 words.
....
5 The landlady informed to us she is increasing the rent.
....
6 Sue blamed that I made a noise, but it was her.
....

1 Choose the correct answers.

1 I feel pretty much .... home with all sorts of pets.
A by B at C to

2 After winning that game, I think we're home and ....
A there B free C dry

3 I did really badly in that last match. It certainly wasn't anything to write home ....
A about B for C over

4 I love staying with my cousins. It's home .... home.
A at B from C to

5 My parents can home .... on the smallest fib.
A on B at C in

6 I told Tom some home .... about his bad behaviour.
A tells B truths C sayings

2 Rewrite the sentences using expressions with *home*.

1 Staying with my grandparents is like being at home.
....

2 Watching those early black and white films really makes you realise how far we've come in cinematography.
....

3 Footballers can earn up to £300,000 per week!
....

4 My new phone is OK but it's nothing special.
....

5 Trudy said some nasty but true things to Tom.
....

3 LISTENING 14 Match the facts in the box with information about the house (1–7). Then listen to the podcast and check.

Fallingwater • $58,000 • Frank Lloyd Wright $155,000 • Bear Run • Edgar Kaufmann $11.4 million

1 the name of the architect ....
2 the name of the owner ....
3 the name of the National Park where it is ....
4 the name of the house ....
5 the cost of the main house ....
6 the cost of the guest house ....
7 the cost of repairs ....

4 14 Listen again and complete the sentences with one to three words or numbers.

- Fallingwater was designed in 1935 and built between **(a)** ....
- It **(b)** .... after it was on the cover of Time magazine in 1938.
- It is on the Smithsonian's Life List of 28 places to visit **(c)** ....
- Kaufmann went to see the architec-'s plans **(d)** .... after he first met Frank Lloyd Wright.
- The house sits on top of a waterfall and is **(e)** .... floors high.
- An interesting feature of the windows is that they haven't got any **(f)** ....
- The two main materials that the house is made of are **(g)** ....
- The main house cost $155,000 to build, which today would be equivalent to **(h)** ....
- The guest house has a **(i)** .... which drains into the river below.
- Every year, there are **(j)** .... where you can study things like poetry and creative writing.

VOCABULARY EXTENSION

5 Match the explanations (a–e) with the expressions (1–5).

1 You don't need to pay – it's **on the house**.
2 After her accident, my aunt was **housebound** for a month.
3 We went to the theatre and there was **a full house**.
4 The police are conducting **a house-to-house** along this road after the burglaries.
5 We've got **a houseful** this weekend.

a unable to leave the house ....
b a detailed search or questioning ....
c every seat was taken ....
d a lot of people staying with us ....
e free ....

6 Choose the correct answers.

1 I was .... by his question. I didn't know what to say.
A floored B walled C shelved

2 I've got a .... tomorrow – how about 10.30?
A door B keyhole C window

3 It's like a(n) .... in here – can I open a window?
A fireplace B oven C radiator

4 Mum takes everything but the kitchen .... when we go on holiday. She's always got a lot of luggage.
A chair B table C sink

5 I'm afraid I've reached my .... I can't pay any more than that.
A ceiling B roof C fence

1 Read the sentences (a–h) and complete the rules (1–2) with these words.

passive reporting verb • present infinitive
reporting verb • verb

a Fallingwater **is said to be** one of the best works of American architecture.

b Wright **was known to have designed** many innovative buildings.

c **It is reported that** Kaufmann was upset initially about the location of the house.

d The views from the balconies **are said to be** spectacular.

e **It has been suggested that** the house has achieved an amazing harmony with nature.

f Restoration of the house **was reported to have cost** over $11.4 million.

g **It is thought that** over five million people have visited it.

h Wright **is reported to have drawn** up the plans in two hours.

There are two different impersonal reporting structures:

1 *It* + ... + *that* + subject + ...

2 Subject + ... + *to* + .../past infinitive.

2 Read the sentences in 1 again. In which sentences:

1 is the reporting in the present?
2 is the reporting in the past or present perfect?
3 is the action being reported in the present?
4 is the action being reported in the past or present perfect?

3 Rewrite the following sentences in two different ways, starting with *It* or a subject noun.

1 They say that the pop star has three swimming pools in his garden.
It is ....
The pop star is ....

2 They believe that the house was built a hundred years ago.
....
....

3 They have reported that the government plans to increase the housing budget.
....
....

4 They have claimed that the building has fallen down.
....
....

5 They think that he paid over £3 million for the house.
....
....

4 Rewrite the sentences using the word given.

1 They reported that the flat has damp problems. **have**
....

2 They know that the builders have repaired the ceiling. **to**
....

3 They say that the house is haunted. **be**
....

4 They have suggested that the previous tenant didn't look after the property. **has**
....

5 They believe that a famous landscape artist designed the gardens. **been**
....

6 They have suggested that the kitchen needs decorating. **it**
....

7 They say that a cleaning company is cleaning the flat. **being**
....

8 They have reported that the house has great furniture. **it**
....

GRAMMAR CHALLENGE

5 Rewrite the sentences so the meaning is the same using the word given.

1 We visited my grandparents every summer when I was a child. **used**
We ....

2 They say that they are building more houses. **said**
More houses ....

3 I usually get up early in summer. **tend**
I ....

4 I won't move into the flat if the landlord doesn't give me a proper contract. **unless**
I ....

5 They have reported that the architect finished the designs yesterday. **to**
.... the designs yesterday.

6 It wasn't necessary for you to phone the landlord. **needn't**
You ....

7 They think the house has a home cinema. **have**
.... home cinema.

8 I have almost finished preparing for my exams. **verge**
I ....

1 LISTENING 15 **Look at the photos. Listen to a student describing one of them. Which one is it?**

A

B

2 15 **Listen again and tick (✓) the things the student mentions.**

1 the people and their relationship ☐
2 what they are wearing ☐
3 what they are doing/have just done ☐
4 why they have done this ☐
5 the place where they are ☐
6 the weather ☐
7 how they might be feeling ☐
8 what they might be going to do next ☐

3 15 **Complete the description with these words. Listen and check.**

apparently • carefully • definitely • generally speaking
maybe • presumably • probably

The picture shows a couple of people, they look as if they're related … they're **(a)** .... mother and daughter because they look quite similar. I'm not sure where they are – **(b)** .... in the garden of their house because there's a large white house in the background or I suppose it could be their allotment as the garden area looks big. They're wearing T-shirts and the mother is wearing a light-weight jacket because **(c)** .... that's what you wear on a sunny day like this. It's **(d)** .... summer time. They're working on the vegetable plot, **(e)** .... they've just picked some of the ripe vegetables very **(f)** .... Maybe some carrots, I think. They look relaxed, **(g)** .... they're quite at home there, so I imagine this is something they regularly do. They seem quite content.

4 **Add the adverbs and adverbials from 3 to the correct section.**

1 **Attitude or opinion**: frankly, honestly, interestingly, luckily, personally, sadly, to be honest, unfortunately, ...

2 **Certainty**: clearly, obviously, probably, undoubtedly, ..., ..., ..., ...

3 **Say what we think of someone else's actions**: carelessly, cleverly, foolishly, kindly, rightly, stupidly, wrongly, ...

5 **Read the questions and answers and replace the phrases with words from 4.**

Q: Why do you think the people have collected these vegetables?

A: Maybe they're going to be used in cooking. **(a)** .... (I imagine that) whoever is cooking dinner has asked them to pick the vegetables. **(b)** .... (I'm very glad) they're not for me, because I **(c)** .... (certainly) don't like vegetables.

Q: What are the pros and cons of having a big garden?

A: **(d)** .... (For me), I think there are a lot of advantages. It's great for children growing up and you can have different areas, for example a vegetable patch, a lawn and flowers. **(e)** .... (To tell the truth), I'm not that interested in flowers, but most people love them. **(f)** .... (Everyone knows that), one of the disadvantages is that you have to spend time looking after it.

Q: What sort of garden do you have or would you like to have?

A: **(g)** .... (It's a pity but) we have a tiny garden. **(h)** .... (To tell the truth), I think my parents are glad because they have so little free time. I'd love to have a country garden, if I could.

6 **Now prepare answers to the questions below for the other photo in 1.**

- Can you describe the photo?
- Why do you think these young people are in the garden?
- What are the pros and cons of teaching young people about growing vegetables during school time?
- Do you think more schools should educate their students about gardening?
- Would this kind of activity be more beneficial for students from the countryside or from cities? Why?

1 Look at the photos of different places and write five adjectives to describe each one.

A

B

2 Read the beginnings of two articles on a travel website and match them to the photos. Then complete them with the correct words. Do the articles include your words from 1?

HOME | DESTINATIONS | DEALS | SEARCH

CITY BREAK

Ask anyone which is the most beautiful city in the world and they'll probably say Paris! In the past, this **(a)** h.................................. city was a **(b)** s.................................. mass of narrow streets and **(c)** s.................................. buildings, but the Paris of today is a **(d)** v.................................. and **(e)** c.................................. city that attracts tourists from all over the world. It is **(f)** r.................................. as a centre for arts, music and theatre.

MORE ▷ ☐

AWAY FROM IT ALL

Fed up with city life? Why not experience the peace and quiet of one of England's most famous beauty spots – the New Forest? This ancient forest lies on the south coast and stretches for hundreds of kilometres. It is a **(g)** m.................................. area of natural beauty with spectacular views of both **(h)** h.................................. and wooded areas, lakes, wildlife and a myriad of **(i)** q.................................. villages.

MORE ▷ ☐

3 Read the continuation of one of the articles and find ...

1. a sentence that catches the reader's attention
2. an example of informal, lively style
3. a direct question to the reader
4. an opinion adverb
5. an amusing closing sentence

HOME | DESTINATIONS | DEALS | SEARCH

➤ continued from page 1

Interestingly, the New Forest dates back to William the Conqueror, who created the forest as a private deer-hunting area. So, if you're into history, there's plenty to learn – there are famous sites to visit as well as museums, and the names of the cafés and inns are also of historic interest!

However, the main attraction of the forest is the wide open spaces where New Forest ponies, donkeys and cows graze without fencing. You can walk through unspoiled countryside across heathland, through old oak woods, along streams and through picturesque villages. Why not stop for a picnic or have a cream tea in a traditional tea shop?

If you're young and think it sounds boring, think again! The forest offers numerous activity courses, including canoeing, riding, tree climbing and so on! So, there's really something for all the family and the accommodation, whether you camp, stay in a bed and breakfast or in an isolated country hotel, will have incredible views. Maybe even a horse poking its nose into your tent in the morning!

4 Read the task and make notes using the plan below.

A holiday website has asked students to contribute online articles about a beautiful area in their country which would be good for people to visit.

Think of a good title

Paragraph 1: Introduction. Say where the place is and why it's popular

Paragraph 2: Talk about an interesting historical/geographical/geological point

Paragraph 3: Mention additional reasons for visiting

Paragraph 4: Talk about whether/how it's attractive for young people/families, etc. Mention accommodation/transport/cost and give a concluding sentence

5 Write the online article. Use vocabulary and expressions from the Writing bank in the Student's Book and the checklist below.

Remember to check:

- you have used a wide range of vocabulary
- you haven't made any grammatical mistakes
- you have used an informal, lively style

Grammar

1 Rewrite the sentences using the correct form of the verbs given.

1 'OK, I made a mistake,' Frank said. **admit**

....

2 'Jason, don't touch the door – I've just painted it,' my dad said. **warn**

....

3 'You didn't check your work, Julia,' the teacher said. **criticise**

....

4 'I wish I'd gone on the trip to Paris,' Mary said. **regret**

....

5 'Why don't we start our own website?' Carol said. **suggest**

....

6 'You got the job! Well done, Penny!' Steve said. **congratulate**

....

7 'We must finish this work before we go,' Leo said. **insist**

....

8 'Rob, you should check the price online,' my mum said. **advise**

....

2 Rewrite the sentences using the words given. Do not change the meaning.

1 My brother says he's cleaned his bedroom, but I don't believe him! **claims**

....

2 Years ago, people thought that the Sun went round the Earth. **was**

....

3 They used to say that smoking was good for your health! **said**

....

4 Experts know that the house was built in 1908. **have**

....

5 People have suggested that the house was badly designed. **it**

....

3 Find and correct five mistakes in the note.

I saw Tom at the weekend and he told that he hadn't seen Ruth since the weekend. He claims to go to her house yesterday, but I don't believe him. He accused to me of not caring and he insisted that we call the police. I don't know why he waited until now, he must call them a few days ago. We spoke to the police and they said that Ruth is reported to have bought a train ticket last Friday. Last week I overheard her to say that she wanted to visit her cousins. If she bought a train ticket, then she's gone to see them. I phoned them and she's there!

Vocabulary

1 Complete the sentences with one suitable word in each gap.

1 I've told the landlord I want to rent the flat. I'm going to put down a .... tomorrow.

2 I bought a flat, I'm looking forward to .... in.

3 We need to buy a table and a bed because the house isn't fully ....

4 My new flat is in really good condition so I don't need to .... it up.

5 I need somewhere to live. Where's the best area to go flat-.................... around here?

2 Rewrite the sentences replacing the words in italics with an expression using *home*.

1 I'm *very comfortable with* old people because I've worked with them before.

....

2 Our dog manages to *find* food wherever you've hidden it!

....

3 The accommodation we had on holiday was nothing *special*.

....

4 When I stayed in Italy *I realised for the first time* how little time we spend eating in the UK.

....

5 With our last goal, we must *have won the competition*!

....

6 How much do you *earn* every month?

....

3 Choose the correct answers.

1 The .... on the plans for the new school has been positive.
A drawback B outback C feedback

2 The view from the window was absolutely breath-.....................
A giving B taking C getting

3 The streets in that part of town are .... because they are rarely cleaned.
A filthy B hilly C sprawling

4 .... account of the increased membership we're going to organise more meetings.
A On B In C By

5 If Pete does this again, I'm going to tell him a few home ....
A realities B facts C truths

6 I'm a landlord and one of my flats is empty. I'm looking for a new ....
A squatter B tenant C lodger

Reading

1 Read the newspaper article. Choose which sentence (a–g) best fills the gaps (1–6). There is one sentence that you do not need.

a After a difficult early start looking for funding, she feels she has established a space 'where youngsters feel safe and valued'.

b She did a business and communications diploma and used it as a springboard to her current venture.

c There, Williams says, her business and administration skills, as well as her connection with young people, blossomed.

d She spiralled downwards, dropping out of school and eventually serving a 28-day custodial sentence.

e However, some of the kids we worked with were in big trouble.

f It's about helping them to find a way to live their lives and feel legitimate.

g Some had never even been out of Birmingham.

From petty crime to small business in one smart move

Justice Williams says her life has changed beyond recognition. Ten years ago, she was 17 and on the cusp of a life in and out of the criminal justice system. She went on to set up her own social enterprise focused on disadvantaged youngsters in Birmingham who are caught up in gang culture or at risk of going to prison.

'I really believe people deserve a second chance,' she says. 'What matters is that young people have the right kind of help. So much depends on what you do with the kids before they offend or if they are at risk of reoffending. **(1)** .... Young people, wherever they come from, are innovative and they are enterprising, but need to know they can be successful.'

Williams is managing director of Inner City Creative Media Group (ICCMG), a social enterprise that trains young people between 17 and 26 in media and business skills. **(2)** ....

She has been able to do it, she says, because of her own experience. Williams, who came from 'a very good background, a nice middle class family in a nice area', found herself at 17 falling in with 'a bad crowd' and living for the first time in the inner city – 'seeing first-hand what deprivation was'. She says that even though she had once been a model pupil, she began to feel 'totally disengaged from society' and drifted into petty crime. **(3)** ....

It was a visit from her siblings, she says, that convinced her 'to rethink what I was doing. I knew then that this wasn't the path I wanted to go down.'

Williams's big chance came when she got involved with a youth group based in Lozells, Birmingham, an area that became notorious when riots thrust it into the media spotlight. Marc Edwards, director of Young Disciples, which works with young people who are particularly hard to reach, gave her a chance to work. **(4)** .... 'I realised I was quite entrepreneurial while I was at Young Disciples,' she says. 'I wanted to put it to good use.'

It was during her two-and-a-half years as a youth worker that she began to understand how she could make a difference to the troubled youngsters she saw every day. 'Some of these kids had real problems. Watching Marc, I learned that by having almost taken the wrong route myself, I could say to these kids: "Look, it doesn't have to be this way."

They seemed to like what I had to say and what we did. We took them to places they had never seen before. **(5)** ....'

Williams says she was deeply affected by the Lozells riots and decided then that, as a young person herself, she might have even more to offer the disaffected youngsters around her. **(6)** ....

If it works as she plans, Williams intends to steer another generation of children away from the prison system. 'It costs £50,000 to send a child to a good school and £50,000 to send one to prison,' she says. 'Why are we so reluctant to spend that kind of money keeping them out of jail in the first place?'

Use of English

2 Complete the text with the appropriate words.

Until recently, I lived at home. Some of my classmates **(a)** .... to find that strange, but I get on really well **(b)** .... my parents and younger brothers. It was good being part of **(c)** .... big, noisy family and I could never live completely alone. However, **(d)** .... being happy at home, I thought it was time to be a bit more independent. After all, **(e)** .... has been said that you don't really become an adult until you leave home. Mum and Dad agreed **(f)** .... I could move out after the initial shock of learning that I was **(g)** .... to be leaving. I found a couple of adverts on the notice board at college but nothing worked out and I was on the **(h)** .... of giving up when I discovered my friend Rob wanted to flat share, too. He thought we **(i)** .... to look together so we went flat-hunting and found a place near the town centre. It was slightly more expensive **(j)** .... I'd originally wanted to pay, but it was perfect for us! **(k)** .... we moved in two months ago, it's been great. Of course, we had a few problems to start with – Rob **(l)** .... to do the washing-up more than once a week. So I threatened **(m)** .... move out! He apologised **(n)** .... not doing it and since then we haven't had any problems. I really like the fact that we're both quite independent, so we don't live in **(o)** .... other's pockets. We enjoy our time together and doing things by ourselves.

Listening

3 LISTENING 16 **Listen and complete the sentences with one to three words and/or a number.**

- People become homeless for different reasons. For example, **(a)** ...., not being able to afford housing, health problems or debt.
- Homeless people have a higher chance of having health problems, low self-esteem and feelings of **(b)** ....
- **(c)** .... % of homeless people in Utah were once considered to be chronically homeless.
- People are considered to be chronically homeless if they have been homeless for a year or **(d)** .... in four years.
- The new policy for homeless in Utah has led to a **(e)** ....% reduction in chronic homelessness.
- All the homeless people now in Utah are known to the authorities **(f)** ....
- The new policy in Utah to reduce homelessness is called **(g)** .... After people are given homes, they **(h)** .... to deal with the problems that caused them to become homeless.
- It costs less than **(i)** .... to help someone through the new policy.
- Other **(j)** .... are already thinking about adopting Utah's policy.

Writing

4 Choose one of these writing tasks. Write between 120 and 180 words.

1 You read the following announcement in an international student magazine.

We will be publishing an issue of the magazine in January called 'Power and responsibility' and we would like readers to send in articles about people they know who hold positions of power or responsibility. Tell us why this person has impressed you and what they have achieved.

Write the article saying:

- Who the person is, how you know them (friend, relative, famous person …) and what they are like
- What the person has achieved
- Why they are an inspiration to you and others

2 Read the article about the closure of a youth centre. Then write a letter of complaint to the local council and request the centre be reopened using the notes below.

YOUTH CENTRE TO CLOSE

Local residents in Hoxton were up in arms to hear about plans to close the Hoxton Youth Centre. The centre is very popular with teenagers and has been praised for its work with young people. Residents have been told that the centre is too expensive to run and they have lodged a complaint about the centre closure, but have had no response. Officials say that the site might be used for a new supermarket.

- at least 30 young people use it every day
- won an award for its programme to help young people get jobs
- some of the funding is through donations, so not that expensive to run!
- there are plenty of supermarkets, but this is the only youth centre! No other place for young people to go

COMMON MISTAKES

5 Correct the mistakes in the sentences.

1. By the end of next week, I have finished my project.
2. I congratulated Natalie for win the competition and asked how she felt.
3. The architect is reported to win a prize for the design of his first building.
4. The court hearing taking place next Monday at 11 am.
5. At this time tomorrow, I am taking my driving test. I hope I pass!
6. They could rob the bank, nobody else could possibly have done it – it was definitely them.
7. He was arrested on the strong of the evidence and sent to prison.
8. It really takes it home to you just how many people are homeless when you see the statistics.
9. Hundreds of years ago, it was thinking that the Earth was flat.
10. The police will keeping an eye on the suspect during the next month.
11. At the end of this year, I will have been study English for ten years.
12. When the police questioned her, she denied to commit the crime.

7 Marketing campaign

Reading

1a VOCABULARY Match the words to sentences 1–6.

banners • billboard • brand name • freebies
marketing campaign • word-of-mouth publicity

1 There are adverts for the car everywhere. ....
2 I was given this on the street. ....
3 The business is doing well because customers have told their friends about it. ....
4 They decided on a company name and logo. ....
5 I hate advertising on websites. ....
6 There's a new one in the high street. ....

1b Circle the correct alternative.

1 Salesmen often *do/make* cold calls in the evening.
2 The company *promoted/launched* a new marketing campaign in August.
3 By *giving/handing* away freebies, advertisers hope to attract more custom for the product.
4 They got a sports star to *endorse/support* it.
5 Do many companies *use/get* word-of-mouth publicity in your country?

1c Complete the sentences.

1 My mum gets really angry with .... callers.
2 The restaurant gets a lot of .... from people who've eaten there.
3 They're getting ready to launch a new TV .... for their latest clothes collection.
4 That website has a .... on every page.
5 They put up a new poster on the ....

2 Look at the photos of anti-advertising. Are the statements True (T) or False (F)? Read the article quickly and check your answers.

1 Anti-advertising is designed to sell more products. T/F
2 Anti-advertising takes place in public spaces. T/F

3 Read the article again and choose the best answer.

1 More and more people ...
   a are exposed to over 130 adverts in less than an hour.
   b are buying products because of advertising.
   c are taking action against advertising in public spaces.
   d remember adverts long after they have seen them.
2 According to the author, the purpose of modern advertising is ...
   a to inform us about products we need to use.
   b to make us feel happy and successful.
   c to explain why one product is better than another.
   d to influence our ideas so we will buy things.
3 People are concerned about advertising in public spaces because ...
   a adverts in public spaces are more influential than others.
   b people cannot choose whether they see it.
   c people are watching fewer adverts at home.
   d they want people to have more control over the content.
4 Brandalism ...
   a was started by two friends who felt insecure and unhappy because of adverts.
   b has carried out two campaigns so far, replacing ordinary adverts with artwork.
   c is planning to recruit more people in ten cities for their next big campaign.
   d has had two five-day anti-advertising campaigns using work by 40 artists.
5 The packing produced by PeopleProducts123 ...
   a was created to show who made a product and how.
   b features people invented by the team of artists.
   c is a response to people criticising how the products were made.
   d gives instructions about how to use the product.
6 In shopdropping, ...
   a people put the new packaging over products and leave photos in supermarkets.
   b people ask to leave items with the new packaging in shops and supermarkets.
   c items with new packaging are secretly left in big shops and supermarkets.
   d people download the packaging and leave it in stores but not in supermarkets.

4 CRITICAL THINKING

To what extent do you feel your life is negatively affected by advertising you see in the street? What would you do to solve the issues the campaigners are protesting about?

5 Match the underlined words with the definitions and explanations.

1 communicate ideas indirectly ....
2 influence the way a situation develops ....
3 after something else happened ....
4 a particular way of thinking about something ....
5 providing people with something they want ....
6 present in every part of something ....

ANTI-ADVERTISING

Advertising in public spaces is everywhere – literally. Every time we step outside our homes, we are bombarded with adverts; they're on the streets we walk down, the places we shop and eat, and the transport we use.

In just one example of how pervasive advertising in public space is, research in London showed that in a 45-minute commute the average person sees over 130 adverts featuring 80 different products, because advertisers pay transport companies huge sums to reach us as often as possible.

However, a growing number of people are now fighting back. They are against advertising in public space because they consider it to be 'visual pollution', something that harms us through our eyes. They believe that even if you do not consciously read an advert, the constant barrage of images has an effect. Seeing them time and time again creates memories and feelings that influence us and encourage us to buy a product at a later date.

To understand why people are concerned, it is necessary to understand modern marketing. In the early days of advertising, adverts focused on explaining that a particular product was cheaper or better than its rivals. Modern advertising, however, aims to shape our understanding of what it means to be happy, beautiful and successful. It is not about catering to existing needs, but creating new desires so that we want new things even when the ones we have are still usable or not used up. We want them because they will make us better-looking, more sophisticated or more successful.

People are particularly concerned about advertising in public spaces because they feel it invades our right to choose whether we see something or not. Unlike when you're at home, where you have a great deal of control over the number of adverts you see, outside the home people have little control over whether they see adverts or not. So, individuals and groups have started 'anti-advertising' campaigns to try to combat the influence that these adverts have.

> **"In a 45-minute commute the average person sees over 130 adverts"**

Brandalism is one such group. It was founded in London by two friends who believe our public spaces belong to the people who live there, not to media companies. They didn't like being constantly exposed to adverts that made people feel insecure and unhappy, so they decided to do something about it. The duo produced artwork the size of posters to make people think about advertising and the messages adverts convey.

In their first campaign, Brandalism spent five days replacing adverts in 36 bus shelters in five cities around the country with their artwork. There was a positive response to the campaign and 16 teams of people were subsequently recruited by the organisers. Their second campaign, Takeover, was more ambitious and took place simultaneously in ten cities around the country. In two days, they did 365 advert 'takeovers', replacing adverts with unsigned works of art by 40 international artists.

The English graffiti artist Banksy, whose real identity is unknown, has also got involved with the anti-advertising movement. He has encouraged people to make adverts their own by altering them. In an online post said to be his, he condemns 'bully' advertisers for making consumers feel small and inadequate. He argues that we need to assert our right to choose whether or not we see any advert in a public space because we have the right not to be made to feel inadequate as a result of something that we see in an advert.

PeopleProducts123 takes a different approach to anti-advertising and instead of changing adverts on billboards, they change the packaging on goods. They believe that we have no idea who makes the products we use or how they do it. They had new packaging created by a team of artists for a variety of products. The new packaging features stories and images about the workers who produce them to remind us that the goods we buy are made by real people. The target of the campaign is large stores and supermarkets. After preparing the new packaging, which has been designed to be easy to print off, participants put it over the original packaging, then place the goods in stores and supermarkets using a technique called shopdropping.

> **"We need to assert our right to choose whether or not we see any advert in a public space"**

Of course, not everyone agrees with the anti-advertising campaigns. Critics say they are subversive and do not represent the feelings or wishes of the majority of people. They argue that these movements are illegal and acts of vandalism, and that adverts fulfil a function because people want to be informed about products. Whether you agree or not, the different campaigns raise an interesting point about our public spaces: who should decide what can or cannot appear there?

1 Match the sentences (a–g) with the descriptions (1–5).

a Every time we step outside our homes, we **are bombarded** with adverts.

b Advertisers **pay** transport companies huge sums to **reach** us as often as possible.

c They didn't like **being exposed** to adverts.

d Sixteen teams of people **were recruited** by the organisers.

e They **had** new packaging **created** by a team of artists.

f The new packaging **has been designed** to be easy to print off.

g People want **to be informed** about products.

1 a passive infinitive ....

2 a passive gerund ....

3 two objects in a sentence ....

4 three examples of verbs in different passive tenses ...., ..., ...

5 causative use of *have* ....

2 Complete the text with passive forms of the verbs given.

Although TV commercials **(a)** .... (now accept) as an inevitable part of our lives, questions **(b)** .... (still ask) about the damaging effect of adverts that **(c)** .... (broadcast) during children's TV programmes. It **(d)** .... (believe) that adverts for fast food can **(e)** .... (blame) for the increase in obesity we are seeing these days. For several years, adverts for fast food and sweets **(f)** .... (ban) in many countries during viewing times for four- to nine-year-olds but for many people this does not go far enough. They insist that the scheduling of adverts for young teenagers too should **(g)** .... (more tightly control).

3 Rewrite each sentence in two ways using the passive.

1 The company has sent a lot of people invitations to the exhibition.

....

....

2 The students gave their teacher a present on her birthday.

....

....

3 They sold us fake perfume at the market.

....

....

4 The shop offered us a reduction if we paid in cash.

....

....

4 Complete these adverts using the correct form of these verbs and the word given.

do • landscape • manicure • service • style

1 Fancy .... (hair) for free? We need models for our trainee hairdressers. Contact us on …

2 Why not .... (garden)? We are experts and charge the lowest prices locally. Give us a call.

3 Don't forget .... (car) regularly. Here at Winn's Garage we have some special summer offers on service rates.

4 .... (someone else) the hard work! Sit back and relax while we cut your lawns and wash your car. No job too small.

5 You will never .... (nails) more professionally than in our new salon in the High Street. Cut-price introductory sessions in May!

GRAMMAR CHALLENGE

5 Find and correct ten mistakes in the advert.

NEW MALL

OPENING ON SATURDAY!

We are pleased to announce that the new shopping mall in Links Road will be open on Saturday 1st August by the Mayor of Hadford. On Saturday, a group of local businessmen and investors will be given a tour of the mall before the mall is being opened to the public. Final preparations are still been made in a few of the stores but workers will finish them by Saturday morning and then the public will be given the opportunity to visit the full range of stores here. Free food and drink will provide in the central café and a magic show with clowns has arranged to entertain children. There will also be the chance to use a brand new service. Get done your shopping for you by one of our 'official shoppers'! Or take advantage of the special offers in the luxury beauty parlour on the second level and enjoy to be pampered for an afternoon! In the evening, the organisers have promised giving a firework display. There is something for everyone at Links Mall, so if you come along, you had a great time!

1 Use the prefixes and suffixes to complete the words.

able • al • ~~ant~~ • ~~auto~~ • con • ful • hood • ible • ic • ify
ion • ise • ish • ism • ity • ive • less • ly • ment • multi
ness • ous • post • pre • y

Prefixes	Suffixes		
auto graph	assist ant	love......	com......
......cert	magn......	skil......	hope......
......pone	act......	cred......	manage......
......-storey	glob......	tall......	original......
......-concert	luck......	collect......	critic......
	neighbour......	danger......	dark......
	invent......	modern......	

2 Use the correct form of the words given to complete the text.

The recent **(a)** .... of a cosmetics advertisement has reignited concerns over the **(b)** .... effects that airbrushing photos of models used in advertising can have. The advert featured a well-known actress, whose **(c)** .... in the photo was younger than in real life. This has become a very **(d)** .... issue and psychologists insist that the **(e)** .... enhanced looks of **(f)** .... people is one of the main factors in the number of young people who suffer from psychological **(g)** .... today. Advertising watchdogs are becoming more alert to this problem, and **(h)** .... for the cosmetics company, they upheld the **(i)** .... Advertisers will need to control the **(j)** .... of their photographers in the future.

WITHDRAW
DETRIMENT
APPEAR
CONTROVERSY
ARTIFICIAL
FAME
ORDER
FORTUNE
DECIDE
CREATE

3 LISTENING ▶ 17 **Listen to an interview with an advertising entrepreneur and tick (✓) the reason she admires Jason Sadler.**

- He has made a lot of money ☐
- He is an expert on using social media ☐
- He uses very unusual advertising methods ☐

4 ▶ 17 **Listen again and choose the correct answers.**

1 Jason Sadler ...
   a has just been nominated for an important advertising award.
   b got paid for changing his surname to advertise a company.
   c has a website to help people change their surnames.
   d permanently changed his surname after selling it.

2 What happened to Headsets.com after Jason changed his name?
   a They made a total profit of $45,000.
   b They spent $6 million less on advertising.
   c They had increased sales worth $250,000.
   d They started specialising in headsets.

3 SurfrApp ...
   a only gives information about the most famous surfing spots.
   b is considering adding weather reports to the app's information.
   c bought Jason's surname for two years.
   d has a variety of information that is useful for surfers.

4 When Jason Sadler set up IWearYourShirt ...
   a he already had a lot of experience in using social media.
   b clients weren't interested in using social media.
   c very few companies advertised on the Internet.
   d most companies had blogs and Facebook pages.

5 In the 1st year, advertising on IWearYourShirt ...
   a cost the same on January 1st as on December 31st.
   b cost more at the end of the year than at the start.
   c doubled each day starting on January 1st.
   d cost $365 for six months.

VOCABULARY EXTENSION

5 Tick (✓) the words that form verbs by adding *-en* or *-n*, and write the verb form. Some words require additional changes.

bright......	long......	soft......
cheap......	loose......	strong......
dark......	narrow......	sweet......
deaf......	red......	thin......
deep......	sad......	tight......
flat......	sharp......	weak......
hard......	short......	wide......
high......	smooth......	worse......

6 Complete the sentences with the correct form of verbs made from adjectives in 5.

1 The council will have to .... the road at the bend because it is too narrow.
2 I've had a big lunch and I need to .... these trousers.
3 Eat a lot of fruit and vegetables to .... your body's resistance to colds and flu.
4 The noise from the explosion was very loud and it nearly .... the people standing closest to it.
5 The sky is .... and that's a sign that rain is on its way.

1 Read the sentences (a–f) and complete the rules (1–7) with the words in bold.

a It's **no** surprise that Sadler came up with a very ingenious pricing policy.

b **Each of** the methods he's used for advertising have been innovative. **None** have been traditional.

c **Every** day he would photograph himself in a T-shirt with the logo of the company.

d **None of** the companies had to pay more than $365 for a day's advertising.

e **All** potential employees had to make a video CV.

f Also, by then **a** large **number of** companies had their own online presence.

1 We use *each* and .... with singular countable nouns. They are followed by singular verbs.

2 We use .... and *every one of* with plural countable nouns.

3 We use .... with plural countable nouns and uncountable nouns. It can be followed by a singular or plural verb if it refers to a plural countable noun.

4 We use .... with singular countable, plural countable and uncountable nouns.

5 We use ...... *(large/small)* .... with plural countable nouns.

6 We use ...., *all of, most, most of* with singular countable, plural countable and uncountable nouns.

7 .... is a pronoun and cannot go with another noun.

2 Circle the correct alternative.

Steve had a birthday party last Saturday. **(a)** A number/Most of guests arrived early and **(b)** every/all person at the party brought a present. **(c)** No/None of his family were there. **(d)** Most/More of the food was provided by a catering company. It was delicious so **(e)** none/no food was left at the end of the party! The house looked great, **(f)** each/every of the rooms had been decorated for the party. **(g)** All/Number of the guests really enjoyed the party.

3 Choose the correct answers.

1 I have a party for my birthday .... year.
A each of B every C most

2 I remember .... the songs that have been used in adverts.
A none B most C all of

3 .... my friends dislike adverts on TV, but some of them enjoy watching them.
A All of B Most of C None of

4 There are a considerable .... adverts on the Internet nowadays.
A number of B each of C every one of

5 I think .... adverts are boring, so I usually turn the sound down.
A most B no C every

6 .... of the actors in the advert is famous. They've all been in many films.
A None B Every one C Every

7 .... adverts should be less than a minute long.
A All of B All C Each

8 Each of the songs .... specially chosen.
A have been B were C was

4 Decide if the sentences are correct. Rewrite the incorrect sentences.

1 I can remember every of detail of the actor's biography.
....

2 None the people I talked to at the concert enjoyed it.
....

3 Matt has no interest in learning about it.
....

4 A number of people has complained about that advert.
....

5 Most the students in my class speak English.
....

6 Each programmes in the series was excellent.
....

GRAMMAR CHALLENGE

5 Complete the text with appropriate words.

It **(a)** .... thought that taking a **(b)** .... risks in our lives is a good thing. I've always wanted to be good at a water sport, so two weeks ago I decided **(c)** .... go water-skiing. I'd **(d)** .... excited about it **(e)** .... several days. **(f)** .... I got to the school, I found there were eight other students in my class. We were given training. **(g)** .... students seemed to understand everything, except me. Then **(h)** .... of us were told we could have a go in the water. As soon as I started, I knew I was in trouble. I'd forgotten **(i)** .... one of the instructions we had been given! I fell in the water and I **(j)** .... get up again. I started shouting for help. When I was on land again, the instructor asked me what had happened. Finally, I **(k)** .... being scared of water. He said I could try again, but I don't think I will. I've tried water sports many times, but **(l)** .... of them have been successful – I've never been able to do them.

1 LISTENING ▶ 18 **Read the task and look at the photos. Listen and put the photos in the order the students talk about them. Which photo do they not talk about?**

Here are some pictures showing people buying things in different places. First talk to each other about the advantages and disadvantages of buying things in these different places. Then decide which place offers the best value for money.

2 ▶ 18 **Listen again. Are the sentences True (T) or False (F)?**

1 Only one student tried to talk to the other. T/F
2 Both students talked about the advantages and disadvantages. T/F
3 One student interrupted the other. T/F
4 One student described a picture without answering the question. T/F
5 They listened to each other carefully. T/F
6 One student's answers were usually too short and simple. T/F
7 They didn't discuss the final decision. T/F

3 **Complete the useful expressions with these words.**

don't • let's • mean • right • see • so • suppose • think

1 What do you .... about (this photo)?
2 Why .... we choose (this photo)?
3 I .... so, but …
4 I see what you ....
5 .... talk about the disadvantages now.
6 Don't you think ....?
7 I .... what you mean, but …
8 Yes, you're absolutely ....

4 **Add the expressions in 3 to the table.**

A Asking for your partner's opinion	1
B Making suggestions	
C Agreeing with your partner	
D Partially agreeing with your partner	

5 **Read the task in 1 again and write the discussion. Use phrases from 3 and try to avoid the mistakes made by the students in the listening.**

1 Complete the useful phrases for writing a report.

Beginning the report

1 The aim/ .... of this report is to outline/ describe/.................... the findings …
2 This report is intended .... …
3 This report is .... on …

Ending the report

4 As I/we have .... mentioned, …
5 My/Our main suggestion/.................... is …
6 Having taken everything into ...., …/ .... things considered, …
7 All .... all, … /To sum ..../ conclude …

2 Read the report on a school charity event quickly and answer the questions.

1 What was the event?
2 Who do you think asked for the report? Why?
3 Are all the comments positive?
4 What is the main recommendation? Why?

A report on the *fashion show*

The purpose of this report is to assess the success of the recent fashion show that was held at Barton Secondary School to raise money for charity and to advise whether a similar project should be organised next year.

CHOICE OF EVENT

The choice of event was excellent because it was interesting for all those involved in the planning and also for the people who came to see it. The display of trendy clothes given by students in the sixth form was well received by the audience and the raffle of one of the most popular outfits raised a large amount for charity.

PROMOTION

The event was fairly well publicised with posters and handouts. However, advertising on local radio could have brought in more people. For some reason it was not put on the school website and this was a costly oversight.

ORGANISATION

In general, the organisation of the event was very good and all the models were well rehearsed. The evening ran efficiently with students clearly positioned to help people with parking and directing them through the school to the main hall. Refreshments had been arranged and were served by younger students from years 10 and 11. This was done quickly and no long queues formed. The event itself was presented by the head teacher and there were no pauses or problems.

CONCLUSION

All in all, the event was a great success and appreciated by everyone who was there. I would strongly recommend organising another fashion show next year. My main suggestion to improve attendance, apart from the previously mentioned lack of publicity, would be to invite a famous model to attend. This would ensure that people from outside our immediate area would come to the event and therefore more money would be donated to charity.

3 Read the report again and find an example of the following:

1 Ten passive forms ....
2 Three phrases from 1 ....
3 A linker ....
4 Three determiners ....
5 An example of formal use of vocabulary ....

4 Read the writing task. Decide how many sections you will need in the report and the key information you will include in each section.

> Your local council wants to know whether to give planning permission for a new shopping centre in your town. It has asked you to write a report on current shopping facilities and to advise them on the need for a new centre. Your report should:
> - outline the current facilities
> - describe which are the most popular shopping places for young people
> - recommend whether the new shopping centre should go ahead or not

5 Write the report. Use phrases from the Writing bank in the Student's Book and the checklist below.

Remember to check:

- you have used the correct style
- you have given each section a title
- you have used useful phrases and expressions

Grammar

1 Complete the sentences with the correct passive form of the verbs given.

A famous cosmetics company **(a)** .... (just report) to the Advertising Standards Authority (ASA). Apparently the photographs of a model in an advert that came out last month **(b)** .... (alter) to make her appear more youthful and this **(c)** .... (not state) in the text that accompanied the advert. It seems that this **(d)** .... (do) more and more often these days and parents and psychologists are concerned that young people's confidence in their appearance **(e)** .... (undermine) by this practice. Apologies from the company involved **(f)** .... (receive) by the ASA yesterday and also assertions that this practice **(g)** .... (more tightly control) in the future. Many people want the practice **(h)** .... (ban).

2 Complete the sentences with the prompts. There is sometimes more than one possible answer.

1 I'm going to .... (Dave/check) my homework before I give it in.
2 Where .... (you/your hair/do)? It looks great!
3 I need .... (my photo/take) for my new passport. Where can I .... (it/do)?
4 We .... (the garage/fit) new tyres before we started the long journey to Scotland.
5 .... (you/vaccinate/your dog) yet?

3 Find and correct the mistakes in the sentences. Some sentences are correct.

1 Every of the contestants was asked the same question.
....
2 None of students in class could answer all the questions.
....
3 Most people I know watch television for a few hours every day.
....
4 I wanted more cake, but there was none of left.
....
5 There was none food in the fridge, so I had to go shopping.
....
6 I am living in this flat for three months.
....
7 When I went to the shop, they had sold most the new phones.
....
8 Matt can't give Lucy your message because he hasn't seen her yet.
....

Vocabulary

1 Complete the sentences with these words.

banners • billboards • brand • endorse
freebies • publicity

1 Do you look at the posters on ....?
2 That company uses word-of-mouth .... to advertise their products.
3 The company give away a lot of .... You don't have to pay for them.
4 They've asked celebrities to .... the perfume.
5 I don't want to see adverts on websites, so .... really annoy me.
6 There are some unusual .... names. I wonder how companies think them up.

2 Complete the sentences with the correct form of the words given.

1 James was very .... when I had a problem. **help**
2 I found the crime drama boring because it was so .... **predict**
3 What is the most .... advert you've ever seen? **innovate**
4 I'm not sure exactly how old Kate is, but she is .... **thirty**
5 Her latest book has been very .... Millions of copies have been sold. **success**
6 The process wasn't slow, it was .... **instant**
7 He's just written an .... about his life. It's fascinating. **biography**
8 That gadget is ...., it can be used to do lots of different things. **purpose**

3 Choose the correct answers.

1 With your black hair, the blue jacket .... you well.
A suits **B** fits **C** matches
2 A lot of people get irritated with companies that make .... calls all the time.
A wet **B** hard **C** cold
3 My mum complains that my clothes are too .... She says they're really untidy, but I like them.
A scruffy **B** trendy **C** sophisticated
4 The flat I rent out is empty. I need to look for a new ....
A lodger **B** tenant **C** landlord
5 We were not at all happy about the fine. We have .... a formal complaint.
A prosecuted **B** lodged **C** suspended
6 A(n) .... is a natural chemical that is produced by plant and animal cells.
A enzyme **B** chromosome **C** species
7 We went to the .... of the perfume company's new marketing campaign.
A start **B** launch **C** opening

8 One life, live it

Reading

1a VOCABULARY Find words in the word search to complete the compound adjectives.

R	O	Q	B	L	O	W	I	N	G	U	Y
Y	A	L	P	V	S	G	Z	N	Q	Y	H
X	M	I	D	Y	N	G	I	L	R	Y	K
X	C	V	S	I	N	Y	E	V	N	M	W
U	D	Y	M	I	O	U	Y	X	S	B	E
C	N	R	N	R	N	E	C	K	P	P	S
T	A	E	T	L	J	G	R	O	L	H	K
W	P	S	C	A	T	C	H	I	N	G	K
O	E	R	G	P	B	I	T	I	N	G	V
D	S	P	L	I	T	T	I	N	G	U	P
O	U	Z	C	J	A	U	L	S	A	U	F
E	J	S	T	O	P	P	I	N	G	P	M

1 ear-..........
2 mind-..........
3 hair-..........
4 heart-..........
5 heart-..........
6 eye-..........
7 eye-..........
8 soul-..........
9 nail-..........
10 break..........

1b Choose the correct alternative.

1 The actress wore a very _eye-opening/eye-catching_ dress to the film premiere.
2 The child's kindness was _soul-warming/heart-warming_. He donated all his pocket-money to charity.
3 I learnt so many new things in the science lecture – it was really _eye-opening/eye-catching_.
4 I was just about to print out my end-of-year project when my computer crashed. It was totally _mind-blowing/soul-destroying_.
5 The noise the crowd made when their team won was so loud it was _ear-splitting/ear-opening_.
6 When the two young boys saw that their football had broken their neighbour's window, they ran away at _break-neck/nail-biting_ speed.

1c Complete the sentences with the compounds from 1a.

1 It was a .... end to the race. We didn't know Rob had won until the officials looked at a photo of the finish.
2 The film was .... It was crazy and powerful and utterly compelling.
3 The science programme was .... It showed me things I'd never thought of before.
4 The new ride at the theme park wasn't fast, but it was .... I'd never been so scared and excited in my life!
5 It was a .... story. I love it when a story has a great feel-good ending.
6 The damage the fire caused was .... after all the hard work we'd done designing and decorating the house.
7 Everyone looked at the poster because it was really ....
8 When a child ran into the road in front of my car it was a .... moment. Luckily, I managed to stop in time.
9 The ambulance got to the hospital really quickly because it drove at .... speed.
10 When the band played, it was .... I didn't expect the music to be so loud.

2 In what order would a skydiver do these things?

a Fall through the air towards the ground.
b Float down to the ground under the parachute.
c Jump out of a plane or helicopter wearing a special suit and a parachute.
d Land safely on the ground.
e Pull the cord to open the parachute.

3 Read the article about a skydiving accident. Six paragraphs have been removed from the article. Choose from paragraphs A–F the one which fits each gap (1–6).

4 CRITICAL THINKING

Why do you think James and his wife don't want to give up skydiving? Do you agree with them?

5 Match the underlined words with these explanations and definitions.

1 extremely happy and excited ....
2 had someone or something as the main or most important interest ....
3 something that is used to support or make something stronger ....
4 affected by emotion in a very powerful way ....
5 a small opening that allows air, smoke or gas to leave a closed space ....
6 measure the amount, strength or speed of something ....
7 a tall narrow shape ....
8 a small window in a camera used to see exactly what you are filming or photographing ....
9 hot gas from boiling water ....

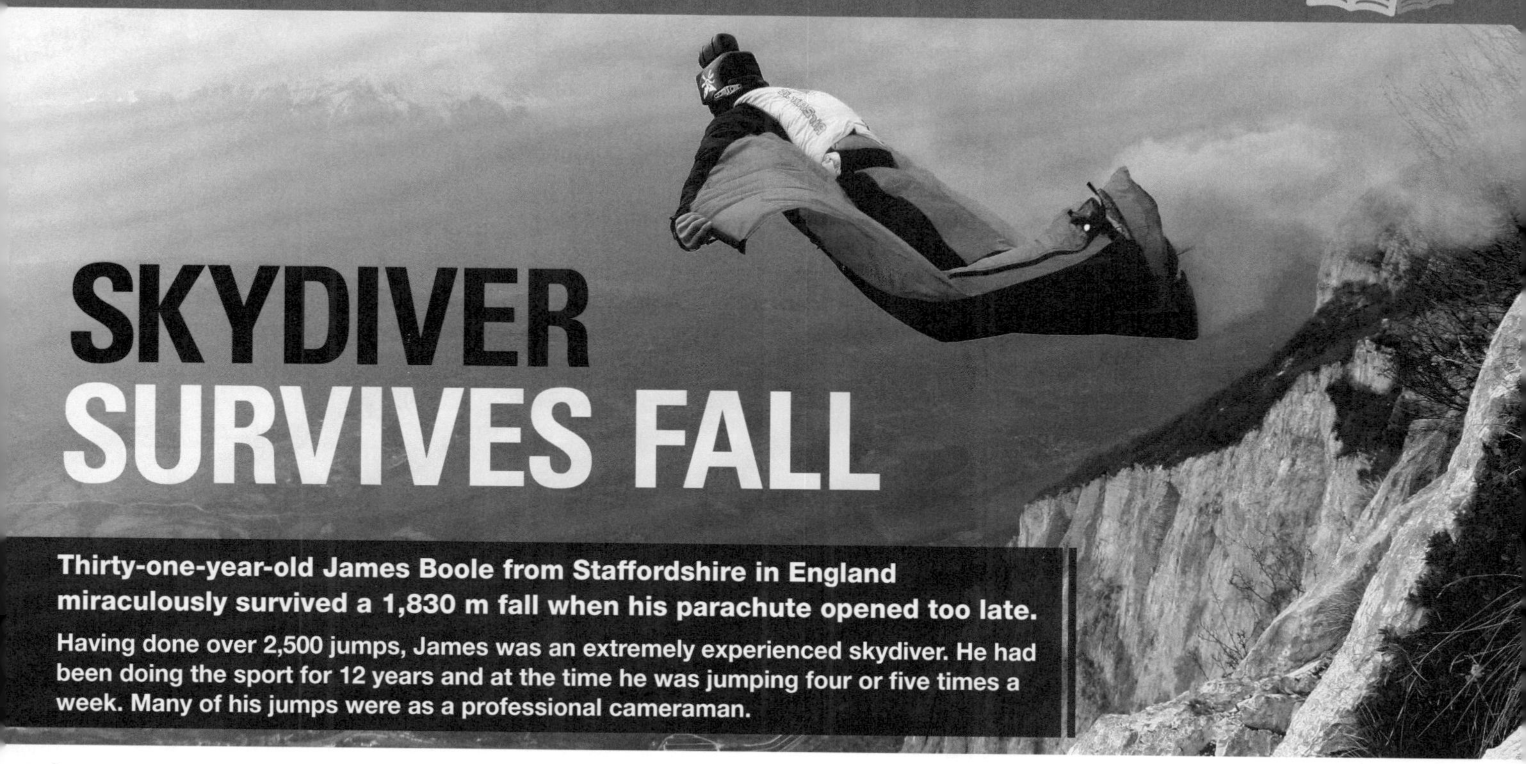

SKYDIVER SURVIVES FALL

Thirty-one-year-old James Boole from Staffordshire in England miraculously survived a 1,830 m fall when his parachute opened too late.

Having done over 2,500 jumps, James was an extremely experienced skydiver. He had been doing the sport for 12 years and at the time he was jumping four or five times a week. Many of his jumps were as a professional cameraman.

1 ....

James and the other skydiver were wearing special suits that allowed them to 'fly' through the air for longer before finally opening their parachutes. The idea was that James would film the athlete flying in front of a column of steam hundreds of metres high that was coming out of a vent in the side of one of the volcanoes.

2 ....

The plan was that the other skydiver would signal to James when it was time to pull the cord to open his parachute at between 150 and 200 metres. But the signal came too late. 'I was very focused on my filming. Quite suddenly, I realised that I could see the texture of the snow and ice, meaning I had two or three seconds before I hit the ground.' James was only 20 metres from the ground.

3 ....

Hitting the ground at 160 kilometres an hour, James landed on his back, leaving a one-metre-deep crater in the snow. The powdery snow and having opened his parachute probably saved his life, but he was knocked unconscious by the impact. When he came round he felt elated at having survived, and terrified. 'I was certain, straight away, that I'd broken my back – the pain in my spine was so immense that I had no doubt about this at all.' Meanwhile, the athlete had floated down under his parachute and landed safely next to him – his parachute had opened at the correct time.

4 ....

It took an hour to reach the local hospital and then another nine hours to fly on to Moscow where a scan confirmed James's back was broken. Luckily, it was a stable fracture and James hadn't suffered any damage to the nerves.

5 ....

While he was recovering from the accident, James spent a lot of time thinking about his life and the impact that skydiving had had on it. 'My whole life has revolved round this extreme sport, this dangerous environment, I've been able to reflect on how it's seen by others and on my motivation for doing it.' His wife, Christina, is also a skydiver and she has jumped since his accident.

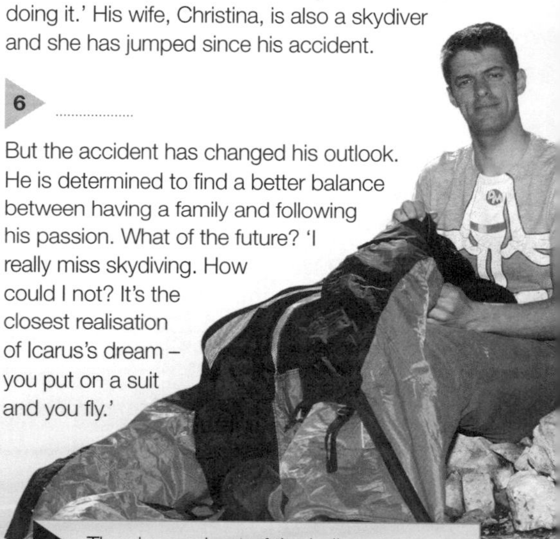

6 ....

But the accident has changed his outlook. He is determined to find a better balance between having a family and following his passion. What of the future? 'I really miss skydiving. How could I not? It's the closest realisation of Icarus's dream – you put on a suit and you fly.'

A 'Terror gripped my heart and stomach. Then I had a clear thought of my wife and three-month-old daughter, and was overwhelmed by sadness as I felt the parachute lift from my back.' Instinctively, James had pulled the cord to open his parachute, and then he felt his feet being pulled up above him.

B Having survived the accident, James nevertheless wants to jump again, too. However, he won't do it for work. 'I'll definitely do one more, and then see how I feel. I think my filming days are over.' He didn't want to completely give up skydiving, which had been such a big part of his life for so long.

C When the accident happened James was working on a television documentary, filming an athlete skydiver over the Kamchatka, a peninsula in the far east of Russia. Known as 'the land of fire and ice', Kamchatka has 29 active volcanoes and is covered in snow for nine months of the year.

D Lying in the snow, James became very cold. He was bleeding and he thought he probably had serious internal injuries. He thought he was about to die. 'I tried to decide what my last words to my family should be – "I'm sorry this has happened, I love you"'. The crew and mountain guides reached James with first aid and a stretcher, but it took time for the helicopter to land and for them to carry him to it.

E They jumped out of the helicopter. Wearing a viewfinder over his left eye to frame the video, James began filming. Because of the snow covering the volcano and having the viewfinder over one eye, it was difficult for James to gauge distances. 'It was very difficult to sense height – all we could see was white,' he remembers.

F James flew back to the UK for further treatment. Fitted with a special metal back brace, he was able to get up and walk within a week. After leaving hospital he had to wear the brace for three months to support his spine and prevent him from making any movements that might damage it while it healed.

1 Match the uses (1–3) with two of the examples (a–f).

1 We use past participles as an alternative to the passive. ....

2 We use present participles to talk about actions happening at the same time. ....

3 We use the perfect form of present participles to say that one activity happened before another. ....

a **Having done** over 2,500 jumps, James was an extremely experienced skydiver.

b **Known** as 'the land of fire and ice', Kamchatka has 29 active volcanoes.

c **Wearing** a viewfinder over his left eye to frame the video, James began filming.

d **Lying** in the snow, James became very cold.

e **Fitted** with a special metal back brace, he was able to get up and walk within a week.

f **Having survived** the accident, James nevertheless wants to jump again.

2 Are these statements about using participles True (T) or False (F)?

1 The subject of the participle clause and the other part of the sentence are often different. T / F

2 Both present and past participles can be used instead of the passive form. T / F

3 The present participle and the perfect form refer to different time sequences. T / F

3 Circle the correct alternative.

1 Striking/Struck by a golf ball, Sam was unconscious for a few minutes.

2 Having walked/Walking in the park, I noticed a lot of people jogging.

3 Speaking/Having spoken to my boss, I left work early for the football match.

4 Playing/Having played tennis all day, I was exhausted.

5 Confusing/Confused by the directions, I took the wrong turning.

6 Distracting/Distracted by the children, Mum forgot to switch on the oven.

7 Having picked/Picking up the broken pieces of glass, I cut my hand.

8 Watched/Watching by his coach, Dan played his best football.

4 Complete the second sentence so that it has a similar meaning to the first sentence. Do not change the word given. Use between three and six words, including the word given.

1 When they told me I had to wait for at least 30 minutes, I decided to come back another day. **been**

.... I had to wait for at least 30 minutes, I decided to come back another day.

2 Jack pretended to understand everything because he didn't want to look silly. **not**

.........................., Jack pretended to understand everything.

3 Poor ticket sales were worrying the organisers and therefore they offered some special deals for groups. **by**

.........................., the organisers offered some special deals for groups.

4 Jenny hoped to impress her interviewers and that's why she wore her best suit. **make**

.... on her interviewers, Jenny wore her best suit.

5 They chose Daniel to play in the final and he went on to score three goals! **after**

.... in the final, he went on to score three goals.

6 You must wear gloves if you use this cleaner on your sports shoes. **when**

.... your sports shoes, you must wear gloves.

7 Miranda's teacher told her off because she had woken up late. **was**

.... told off by her teacher.

8 We won the tennis match easily and then we had a good celebration. **after**

.........................., we had a good celebration.

GRAMMAR CHALLENGE

5 Find and correct the mistakes. Some sentences are correct.

1 I was determined to improve my game after having watched the match on TV.

2 By 8 pm I'll have being working for eight hours.

3 Having left in the sunshine, the ice cream quickly melted.

4 I needn't have worried about doing the interview – I got the job.

5 When doing an extreme sport you often need to wear special safety equipment.

6 We can't afford buying a new car, although our old one keeps breaking down.

7 I can learn to drive now, been seventeen.

8 Given out a test, the teacher left the classroom for five minutes.

1 Rewrite the sentences using the word *point* in each.

1 I understand what you're saying.
I see your point.

2 You've shown that your idea works!

....

3 What's the main thing you want to say?

....

4 I was just about to call you.

....

5 I partially agree with you.

....

6 You've misunderstood me.

....

2 Write words for these definitions.

1 extra money you give someone for a service ....
2 your money is in this in a bank ....
3 1–1 in a football match ....
4 difficult ....
5 obvious ....
6 short time to relax ....

3 Match the answers in 2 to another meaning.

1 create a picture *draw*
2 a useful suggestion ....
3 separate into pieces ....
4 description or report of something ....
5 not soft ....
6 (of the sky) without clouds or rain ....

4 LISTENING 19 You are going to listen to five people talking about happiness. Look at the two listening tasks. Listen and complete both tasks at the same time.

Task 1: For questions 1–5, choose from the list (A–H) the thing each speaker did to increase their happiness. There are three extra letters which you do not need to use.

1 Speaker 1 ....
2 Speaker 2 ....
3 Speaker 3 ....
4 Speaker 4 ....
5 Speaker 5 ....

A I started doing a new job.
B I did a course that changed my life.
C I got into shape and noticed the benefits.
D I tried a technique recommended by a health specialist.
E I volunteered at an organisation.
F I gained self-confidence.
G I took medication which helped me.
H I changed my sleeping habits.

Task 2: For questions 6–10, choose from the list (A–H) the biggest benefit each speaker found. There are three extra letters which you do not need to use.

6 Speaker 1 ....
7 Speaker 2 ....
8 Speaker 3 ....
9 Speaker 4 ....
10 Speaker 5 ....

A feeling better about himself/herself
B feeling more optimistic and upbeat
C more compassionate
D more decisive and energetic
E feeling braver
F clarity of thoughts
G gratitude for his/her life
H less anxious

5 19 Listen again. Are the statements True (T), False (F), or is the information Not Mentioned (NM)?

1 If you do no exercise, no endorphins are released into the body. T / F / NM
2 The hippocampus is responsible for processing positive experiences. T / F / NM
3 Having a lot of money can always make us happier. T / F / NM
4 When you smile you feel happier and you feel pain less. T / F / NM
5 Meditation really only helps with stress levels. T / F / NM

VOCABULARY EXTENSION

6 Think of one word only which can be used to complete each set of three sentences.

1 There's a .... on this shirt, so I'll have to take it back to the shop.
I got a good .... for this test.
People used to say 'Sir' as a .... of respect.

2 My grandfather .... a business for 20 years.
The athlete .... the race in record time and won.
I had to order some printer ink because I .... out.

3 Pete's socks don't .... again!
We'll need a .... to light the campfire.
I thought the tennis .... was really nail-biting.

4 What do you get if you add up all the .... numbers under 20? Quick!
.... Janet couldn't translate the sentence – it was so hard!
No more fighting you two – you're .... now, let it rest!

5 The waiter took our .... and then we had to wait half an hour for the food.
The soldier refused to obey the .... to put down his gun.
The child put her toys on her bed in .... of size, from smallest to biggest.

1 Look at the examples and complete the rules with these words.

as • can • changes • comparative • countable
modify • must • superlatives • uncountable

1 We use *less* with ………………… nouns and *fewer* with ………………… nouns.
   - Far fewer people do sufficient exercise nowadays.
   - I spend less time worrying about things.

2 We use *as … as* to say two things are the same. We use *not as … as/not so … as* to say the second person/thing is more … than the first. After a negative, we ………………… use *so* or *as*. However, in a positive sentence we ………………… use *as*.
   - I wasn't nearly so active as I used to be.

3 After the expression *(not) the same …* we use ………………… to finish the comparison.
   - It's not the same doing things for yourself as doing them for others.

4 We use double comparatives to talk about continuing ………………….
   - Life just gets better and better.
   - More and more people are taking up meditation to help reduce stress.

5 We use *the* + comparative, *the* + ………………… to talk about two things that happen together.
   - The better I get at meditation, the more aware I am of my feelings.

6 We can use *slightly, considerably, a bit, a lot, a great deal, much, far, twice/three times*, etc. to ………………… comparatives.
   - Having more money did not make me a great deal happier.
   - I got considerably stronger.

7 We can use *by far, easily, by a long way* to modify ………………….
   - I found that by far the most important thing for improving low mood was regular exercise.

8 We can use *quite, nearly, almost, just, twice/three times, nowhere near, nothing like* to modify *(not) as … as*.
   - It wasn't nearly as difficult as I'd imagined.

2 Circle the correct alternative.

1 The higher the jump, the *more/most* exciting the skydive is.
2 My friend Sally has the same sports instructor *than/as* you.
3 At this time of year, the evenings get *long/longer* and longer and it stays light until *considerably/quite* later.
4 Bungee jumping is the *scarier/scariest* sport I know.
5 The event was *almost/slightly* as interesting this year as last year.
6 We tend to drink far *less/fewer* water than we should.
7 I believe meditating is slightly *better/best* for you than doing exercise.
8 I think skydiving is *by far/far* the most exciting sport I've ever done.

3 Rewrite the sentences starting with the words given.

1 Greg has played more basketball games than I have this season.
   I …………………
2 You'll get fitter if you work out more often.
   The …………………
3 It's quieter in the countryside than it is by the beach.
   It isn't …………………
4 A hotel gives you more comfort than a tent.
   A tent doesn't …………………
5 It takes more time to cycle to the forest than it does to go by car.
   Going by car …………………

GRAMMAR CHALLENGE

4 Complete the second sentence so that it has a similar meaning to the first sentence. Do not change the word given. Use between three and six words, including the word given.

1 I get confused by the number of different road signs on this short stretch of road. **what**
   ………………… the number of different road signs on this short stretch of road.
2 The new advertising campaign for sportswear really impressed me. **by**
   ………………… the new advertising campaign for sportswear.
3 We must hire someone to replace this cracked window. **replaced**
   We ………………….
4 The number of speed cameras has decreased a lot this year. **far**
   There ………………… this year.
5 'What have you been working on?' Dave asked. **me**
   Dave asked ………………… on.
6 You'll be happier if you do more exercise. **more**
   …………………, the happier you'll be.
7 I haven't seen Diana for about three weeks. **last**
   I ………………….
8 My strength has increased a lot compared to how it used to be. **considerably**
   I am ………………… to be.
9 Don't do the last exercise if you haven't got time. **unless**
   Don't do the last exercise ………………….
10 Jason is a better footballer than Alex. **as**
   Alex is ………………… Jason.

1 LISTENING 20 **Match the photos (A–C) to the activities. Then listen and put the activities in the order they are mentioned.**

A

B

C

sailing ☐
horse-trekking ☐
skateboarding in a skate park ☐

2 20 **Listen again. Are the sentences True (T) or False (F)?**

1 Marta thinks that skateboarding would be a bit boring. T/F
2 She thinks horse-trekking is worth the expense. T/F
3 She doesn't think the friend would have fun sailing. T/F
4 She believes spending time with friends is more important than spending money. T/F
5 She says that planning things is never necessary. T/F
6 She describes a time when her mum made a spontaneous decision. T/F

3 20 **Circle the correct alternative to complete the useful phrases. Listen again and check.**

1 _Allow/Let_ me see …
2 How can I _put/make_ it …?
3 I suppose that _what/which_ I'm saying is …
4 In _other/different_ words …
5 What I _said/meant_ was …
6 Let me _think/reflect_ about that for a second …
7 The _word/truth_ is …

4 **Look at the photos. What are the good and bad points of each type of camping trip? Make notes in your notebook.**

A

B

C

5 **Read the exam task and answer the questions.**

A British friend is coming to stay with you for two weeks. You want to take him/her on a weekend camping trip. You have these types of camping trips to choose from.
Choose the type of camping trip that in your opinion is the most suitable and explain your choice.
Explain why you have rejected the other two.

1 Do you think it's better to plan trips like this or make your decisions at the last minute? Why?
2 How important do you think it is to have a lot of money to enjoy a holiday?

6 **Now write your answer to the task in 5. Try to use the phrases from the Speaking bank in the Student's Book.**

1 Read the essay question and the answer. Put the paragraphs in the correct order.

> **Some people say that it is important to encourage children to do competitive sports at school. Others disagree and say that this can be a bad thing. Discuss both these views and give your own opinion.**

A ☐
On the other hand, there are those who not only disagree but also disapprove. In their opinion, it can be very damaging to a young person to be exposed to failure time and time again in sport. Physical weakness that becomes apparent in competitive sport can expose children to bullying and lower their general confidence. These people believe that sport should be on the curriculum to help improve a child's health, not to develop a competitive spirit.

B ☐
There is no doubt that we live in a world where competition is increasingly important. There seems to be an element of competition in nearly every aspect of our lives, from getting a job to winning a contract for a company. Individual success depends on beating others somewhere along the route. Does it follow that encouraging competitive sports is a good way to prepare children for the competitive world they will enter on leaving school?

C ☐
Whilst I agree that too much competition can be demotivating – I am sure we have all at some time experienced the humiliation of NOT being chosen for a team in front of our peers – my opinion is that competition is something that comes naturally to children. All in all, as long as opportunities for competition in sport are provided for children without an excessive emphasis on winning, I think it can only be a good thing. After all, as well as encouraging winners, it also helps us learn to accept defeat and profit from the experience – a very important lesson for later on in life.

D ☐
Many people believe that it is. They say that participating in competitive sports at school helps develop the competitive instinct that will help young people later in life. It teaches a certain level of fighting spirit and reinforces the need to come out on top. What is more, school is a relatively friendly environment in which to practise this and early failures will not have dire consequences.

2 Find words or phrases in the essay in 1 that mean the following:

1 although ....
2 however ....
3 anyway ....
4 in addition to this ....
5 is it therefore true that …? ....
6 it is certain that … ....
7 if … ....
8 beneficial ....

3 Complete the phrases in the table.

Introducing and sequencing arguments
First and .... / Last but not ....
Adding arguments
Furthermore / Moreover / Not only … but .... / What is ....
Making contrasts and giving counterarguments
On the .... hand … on the other hand / Despite the .... that
Expressing consequences
As a ....
Expressing strong personal opinions
.... my mind / There's no .... that / As .... as I'm concerned
Expressing general or other people's opinions
It is .... accepted that / Some people .... that
Concluding
All .... all / To .... up

4 Read these comments about professional sports stars earning high salaries. Which are for (F) and which are against (A) it?

1 It's appalling that footballers get paid so much. They do really little compared with most of us who work. ....
2 These high salaries mean that tickets to watch matches and events are too expensive for normal local people to afford. ....
3 Sports stars are entertainers today – they deserve to get paid like other celebrities. ....
4 These sports stars have no loyalty to their club or fans, they just go where the money is good. ....
5 Sports stars train hard and are talented. Why shouldn't they be extremely well-paid? ....

5 Read the essay questions. Which is an opinion essay (O) and which is a for-and-against essay (F/A)?

1 Some people say that professional sportsmen earn salaries that are much too high. Others disagree and say that they deserve to be paid highly. Discuss both these views and give your own opinion.

2 'Professional sportsmen shouldn't earn such high salaries.' Do you agree with this statement?

6 Choose one of the essays to write. Use the ideas in 4 and/or your own ideas and expressions from the Writing bank in the Student's Book. Remember to check your work.

Grammar

1 Complete the sentences with the correct form of the verbs.

drive • get • see • trap • want • watch

1 .... in the cave by the rising water, they wondered how they might be able to get out.

2 .... down our road, I saw that a tree had fallen onto my neighbour's fence.

3 .... to get home as fast as possible, I took a taxi from the station.

4 .... permission to leave school early, I went to get my teeth checked at the dentist.

5 .... the chocolate bars, my baby sister started shouting, 'I want some! I want some!'

6 .... by the crowd, the team did really well and won the match.

2 Circle the correct alternative.

1 I think I have the same opinion as/that you.

2 He's considerably/easily the most intelligent person I know.

3 In my opinion historical films are by far/far more interesting than westerns.

4 The more you practise, the more easy/easier it gets.

5 It'll soon be winter and the weather is getting cold/colder and colder.

6 Riding horses can be as/so tiring as riding a bike.

7 There are far fewer/less green spaces in cities than in the country.

8 It's not the same playing football indoors than/as playing outside.

3 Find and correct the mistakes in the sentences. Some of the sentences are correct.

1 The second film in the series isn't so interesting than the first.

....

2 This computer game isn't near as much fun as the last one.

....

3 Your essays are getting more and more as interesting.

....

4 The faster I write the worse my handwriting gets.

....

5 People nowadays have to be inform about technology.

....

6 I think that walking is slightly the best for your health than cycling.

....

7 These products will be promoted using far more social media than usual.

....

Vocabulary

1 Complete the compound adjectives.

1 a nail-.................... finish to a race

2 an eye-.................... outfit

3 an ear-.................... scream

4 a mind-.................... revelation

5 a soul-.................... job

6 a hair-.................... theme park ride

7 a break.................... speed

8 a heart-.................... happy story

2 Rewrite the second sentence so that it has a similar meaning to the first sentence, using the word given.

1 Now, I think we should stop and have a coffee. **point**

....

2 I would like you to look at the rules for using participles. **attention**

....

3 We must consider all aspects of the issue. **take**

....

4 I missed what the lecturer said at the end of the talk. **catch**

....

5 I was really upset when my dad sold our old car. **broke**

....

6 My friend's mum is going to collect us after the concert. **pick**

....

3 Choose the correct answers.

1 The documentary about the environment was eye-.................... I was surprised by many of the things I learnt.

A catching **B** watering **C** opening

2 I've lost a lot of weight since my illness and this skirt is too .... now.

A tight **B** plain **C** loose

3 Doing the bungee jump was heart-.................... .

A warming **B** stopping **C** raising

4 I'm not going to have a race with you just to make a ....

A point **B** mark **C** noise

5 Are you going to the .... of the new marketing campaign?

A beginning **B** launch **C** opening

6 You don't understand, you've completely .... the point.

A proved **B** missed **C** got

Reading

1 Read the article and choose the best answer.

1 The man the writer saw on the zip wire while he was in Pepe's car …
   a was falling into some trees.
   b was screaming in fear.
   c was travelling fast towards a cliff.
   d was already on the ground.

2 The flying zip wire in Pietrapertosa …
   a goes from the village over a canyon to a village in the next valley.
   b is one of the three most popular zip wires in Italy.
   c attracts 6,000 more visitors than any other one in Europe.
   d was started three years ago as a way of saving the village.

3 According to the writer, Pepe …
   a says the scenery is extremely attractive.
   b is a slim man in his 60s who is very calm.
   c has a very important job calming people down.
   d owns the company that operates the zip wire.

4 During his first ride on the zip wire, the writer …
   a notices the speed he is travelling at most of all.
   b feels calm and is able to enjoy the views.
   c hardly notices when the ride comes to an end.
   d took only five seconds to cover the distance.

5 After the first ride, the writer …
   a had to walk back up the mountain to do another ride.
   b travelled by minibus and donkey to repeat the same ride.
   c didn't want to return to the noise and pollution of city life.
   d had no worries about trying another similar ride.

MAN ON WIRE

Pepe's Fiat was charging around the helter-skelter curves on the mountainside as we heard the first screams. Suspended above the car, yelling with unfettered excitement, was a man flying towards the cliff face to our left and disappearing into the hillside.

'Don't worry,' grinned Pepe, 'the trees will break his fall.'

We'd arrived at Pietrapertosa – a village of 500 flinty houses hugging a craggy hillside at the southern end of the Apennines. Three years ago this stony hamlet, whose population was declining rapidly, realised its precipitous position could be its salvation. A wire was stretched across the 1,000 metre-high, 1,500 metre-wide canyon that separates Pietrapertosa from its neighbouring village, and the world was invited to come and fly across the valley. It is Italy's only flying zip wire, one of just three in Europe, and now attracts around 6,000 people a year.

'Don't worry,' grinned Pepe, 'the trees will break his fall.'

Pepe, who worked for the company offering the experience, had the job of easing the fears of this shaky visitor before his flight. 'This is a very stunning place,' said the stout sexagenarian. 'If you are going to throw yourself off a cliff, there is no more charming place to do it than the Apennines.' You couldn't deny his logic. The spectacular cracked granite outcrops reach into the sky like gnarled fingers, bearers of evocative nicknames such as Owl's Beak and Lizard's Toe.

I hung in mid-air, staring into the void.

Pietrapertosa has tried to calm visitors by naming its cliff-top leap the Flight of the Angel (Il Volo dell'Angelo).

I passed my now rather clammy ticket to the smiling Elena who prepared me for the flight, trussing me up in a PVC harness. 'Do many people decide not to fly at the last moment?' I asked hopefully. 'No,' replied Elena. 'Once they pay the €30, they don't want to waste their money.'

With a tug I was lifted into the starting position. I hung in mid-air, staring into the void. 'Buon Volo!' said Elena, and then I was away, soaring over the chestnut trees. The ground fell away and I was 1,000 m up in the air. Adrenaline fired though me, then as the landscape rolled below with a gentle hypnotic rhythm, I felt an overwhelming sense of tranquillity. Fields, farms and rivers seemed held in time. Apart from the wind in my face, there was no sense that I was travelling at 70 kph. No sense, that is, until I crunched into the braking system on the other side of the valley. From 70 kph to nought in five seconds: welcome to the village of Castelmezzano.

I'd travelled a kilometre across the valley from Pietrapertosa – and spent two minutes with the angels. The walk back to Pietrapertosa is a rugged two-hour hike, but fortunately Il Volo dell'Angelo is a return trip, so I was taken up the valley by minibus and, for the final kilometre, by Lucia the donkey, to another departure point.

Flying now seemed the natural way to travel – no jams, no pollution, no noise.

This time I threw myself off the 400 m cliff with no fear. Flying now seemed the natural way to travel – no jams, no pollution, no noise. Then I felt a pulsing sensation against my chest: not my heart's final protests, but my mobile phone ringing. If only I hadn't been strapped in: 'Hi. Where am I? I'm flying with the angels.'

Use of English

2 Complete the text with the correct form of the words given.

You might not have heard of Bianca Guimaraes, but she is one of the **(a)** .... new talents in advertising. Bianca was born in Brazil and as a child she was very **(b)** .... and she had plenty of **(c)** .... She always knew she wanted to go into advertising. — HEAT, CREATE, IMAGINE

She has just finished working on a hugely **(d)** .... augmented reality app for an advertising campaign. The app works with sticking plasters featuring the TV show characters the Muppets. After children have had a plaster stuck on a cut, they can take a picture of it on a phone with the app and the character on the plaster comes to life. The Muppets are already **(e)** .... popular with children so **(f)** .... they love the app. — SUCCESS, INCREDIBLE, SURPRISE

Advertisers like Bianca are always trying to find exciting and **(g)** .... ways to reach their audiences. Campaigns like this which are able to catch the target audience's **(h)** .... because they are so **(i)** .... are the kind of campaign every young advertiser dreams of creating. With Bianca's talent, the **(j)** .... is that she will go on to produce many more memorable campaigns. — INNOVATION, ATTEND, ORIGIN, LIKELY

Listening

3 LISTENING 21 **Listen to five people talking about an experience related to advertising. Look at the two listening tasks and complete both tasks at the same time.**

Task 1: For questions 1–5, choose from the list (A–H) what the speaker says about advertising. There are three extra letters which you do not need to use.

1 Speaker 1 ....
2 Speaker 2 ....
3 Speaker 3 ....
4 Speaker 4 ....
5 Speaker 5 ....

A I was persuaded by an advertising campaign to buy something I didn't really need.
B I create adverts to be used on social networking sites.
C I don't really see the point of advertising.
D My work was recognised and appreciated.
E I had a job in advertising that I found really boring.
F I won an award in a competition for best advert.
G I am finding it hard to completely escape from online advertising.
H I made a big mistake during an advertising campaign.

Task 2: For questions 6–10, choose from the list (A–H) what each person felt. There are three extra letters which you do not need to use.

6 Speaker 1 ....
7 Speaker 2 ....
8 Speaker 3 ....
9 Speaker 4 ....
10 Speaker 5 ....

A annoyed
B worried
C regretful
D optimistic
E embarrassed
F relieved
G amused
H indifferent

Writing

4 Choose one of these two writing tasks. Write between 120 and 180 words.

1 'All young people should be encouraged to try new sports, including extreme sports.' Do you agree with this statement?

2 An advertising company wants to know whether it should increase its online advertising or not. You have been asked to write a report. Read the results of a survey you carried out at school and then write your report.

Do you find online adverts annoying?	68% yes	32% no
Do you remember and talk about online adverts with your friends?	16% yes	84% no
Do you remember and talk about other adverts (not online)?	76% yes	24% no
Have other adverts (not online) introduced you to a product you then went on to buy?	56% yes	44% no
Have online adverts introduced you to a product you then went on to buy?	23% yes	77% no

COMMON MISTAKES

5 Correct the mistakes in the sentences.

1 My dog doesn't like telling what to do by anyone but me!
2 Most of the people I invited came to my party, and every of them bought me a present.
3 Designing to appeal to children, the advert was successful in getting parents to buy the toy.
4 I'm having my hair cutting tomorrow.
5 Young people nowadays spend considerably fewer time outdoors than they used to.
6 My friend Paul is tallish and he's very funny and optimist.
7 It's not the same seeing a film in the cinema that seeing it on TV.
8 Having just start the book, I didn't know if I was going to enjoy it yet or not.
9 In my opinion, the new advert is by far more interesting than the last one.

Reading

1 VOCABULARY **Read the clues and complete the crossword.**

Across

3 I'm hoping to .... on a degree course.

6 My sister is following in our mother's ...., she's going to become a doctor like Mum.

8 It's important to have drive and .... if you want to succeed in business.

10 Carlo started as an office assistant and .... up running the company.

11 Work experience gives you .... into the practicalities of the workplace.

12 My father wanted to .... on in life and be a success.

14 After I decided to study engineering I never .... back. It was the best thing I ever did.

Down

1 Many students decide to .... an apprenticeship rather than going to university.

2 It took Dave a while to .... in when he moved jobs.

4 James has a list of things he wants to do and he plans to .... them all this year.

5 After I started my new job it took me a while to find my ....

7 Sarah is willing to try her .... at anything.

9 When you start your own company, you often have to overcome many ....

13 Women used to put their careers on .... when they had children, but that's changing now.

2 Read the introduction on page 77 and answer the questions.

1 What are STEM careers?

2 Do more girls or boys go into these careers?

3 Read the article. For questions 1–10, choose from the people (A–D). The people may be chosen more than once.

Who …

- doesn't work professionally in her field? **1** ....
- has helped secondary school students with a project? **2** ....
- is still studying as well as working? **3** .... **4** ....
- thinks her profession will be extremely important in the future? **5** ....
- does unpaid work with a group of professionals? **6** ....
- worked in another field before starting in her STEM job? **7** ....
- was very proud of the work her students did to help a child? **8** ....
- did some projects when she was at school that inspired her career choice? **9** ....
- taught herself about her subject when she was a young girl? **10** ....

4 CRITICAL THINKING

Why is it important to encourage girls to study subjects that are traditionally considered to be for boys, and to encourage boys to study subjects that are traditionally considered to be for girls?

5 Match the underlined words with the definitions.

1 equipment or technology that uses the newest and most advanced ideas and features ....

2 caused a strong emotion or reaction ....

3 write a set of instructions that a computer can understand ....

4 too much ....

5 help and give advice to a younger or less experienced person, especially in a job or at school ....

6 caused the start of something ....

WOMEN IN STEM: CASE STUDIES

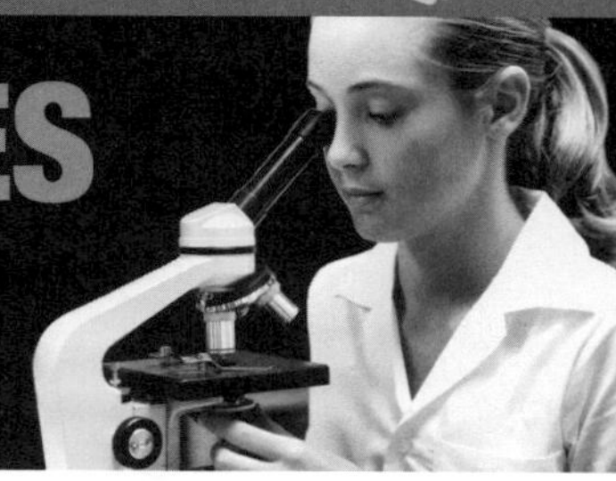

There are still far fewer women in STEM (Science, Technology, Engineering and Maths) careers than men. Here we look at the experiences of four women who work in these fields.

A VEDIKA DALMIA

VEDIKA DALMIA is a software developer at Bloomberg, a financial information and technology company.

Vedika grew up in India and she was lucky enough to have access to excellent computer science teaching at a young age, with a focus on practical learning. She took part in several projects to build robots and program them to do tasks, and this sparked her interest in programming.

Vedika studied computer science at university, but she believes it's important to keep learning. 'New technologies are being developed all the time. My company runs intensive training courses which I found really helpful.' She also goes to lectures and technical talks and studies with books. 'I find having a "study buddy" helps and if you are stuck you can always get help on an online community forum.'

Recently, Vedika started volunteering with Ladies Who Code, a monthly meet-up group for women programmers to share knowledge and ideas. They now have over 1,000 members in the UK and the US and they also organise events for women who want to learn.

Vedika loves working in the tech world: 'It is impossible to get bored; there's always something new to learn and lots of brilliant and passionate people to draw inspiration from.'

B ANNA SHAW

ANNA SHAW left school at 17 and started work in a customer service role, but she wasn't finding her job challenging enough.

By chance, she spotted an apprenticeship at a pharmaceutical company when she was browsing online, and decided to apply: 'I'm a very hands-on type of person and prefer to physically learn the skills whilst getting the technical knowledge.'

Now the only female science apprentice at her company, Anna works in the laboratory testing materials using state-of-the-art equipment, as well as doing a distance-learning degree at Manchester Metropolitan University, one of the only two girls in her year.

Anna became a STEM Ambassador hoping to inspire the next generation of female scientists. She gives careers talks and goes to science fairs. 'I love being able to tell girls that you don't have to be male to be in this industry, all you need is passion and confidence, and the ambition to achieve.' She was selected to do a presentation for the British prime minister to show how she promotes STEM careers using interactive experiments.

Last summer she volunteered to mentor a group of secondary school students for a 14-week Engineering Development Trust project, sharing her expertise. The group of four boys and four girls did a project about mental well-being – and won a prize! She says it was 'one of the best things I've done so far.'

C THERESA COOPER

THERESA COOPER first became interested in astronomy when she was eight, after reading a book about it which fired her imagination. She lived in a small village in Wales and used to go out on her own at night, teaching herself the constellations.

After studying computer science, she got a job with the Natural Environment Research Council in the oceanography division. For three months each year she worked on the research ships *Discovery* and *Shackleton*, to provide software support – and she was usually the only woman on board. Her job took her to many places, including Antarctica, Iceland and the Caribbean, and she continued star-gazing whenever she could.

Now she devotes a lot of her time to amateur astronomy and has visited most of the world's largest observatories and the NASA centres. She helps to run the Cardiff Astronomical Society and through it has met many of the UK's famous astronomers.

Theresa is an active member of the Campaign for Dark Skies which campaigns against excessive and irresponsible lighting in order to restore the beauty of the night sky. 'My favourite aspect of astronomy is to look at the panorama of stars with the naked eye,' she says. 'The sky above us is 50% of our environment. We should also look up and appreciate the night sky. It's amazing.'

D ELENA RODRIGUEZ-FALCON

ELENA RODRIGUEZ-FALCON is a professor of Engineering at Sheffield University. Born in Mexico, she studied mechanical engineering and then went on to work in the engineering industry there. Elena also has a degree in business.

When she moved to the UK she was shocked to find only 7% of women study engineering, compared to over 35% in Mexico. Keen to do something about it, she co-founded the first University Women in STEM network. In her new role as director of Women in Engineering at the university, she has helped female staff to be more proactive in their careers, which in turn develops stronger role models.

Elena believes it is essential to influence girls from a much younger age. 'Engineering is perceived as a male-oriented discipline. We're working really hard with the government, the media, other universities and schools to raise awareness that engineering is a fantastic career for women,' she says. She believes engineering is a profession that will be essential to tackle the problems that face humanity.

The module 'Make a Change', where students work with families and organisations to solve a practical problem, is one of her proudest achievements. In the first year, they had to help a young boy with severe physical disabilities. 'The students were incredibly professional,' Elena remembers. 'They came up with solutions that were not only technically outstanding, they were commercially viable. And that's why I love being an engineer and why I love being a teacher.'

1 Complete the table with rules 1–11.

Use *the*	Use *a/an*	Do not use an article
1		

1 when there is only one thing or person
2 with an adjective to talk about a group
3 with uncountable nouns to make general statements
4 to refer to a thing or person for the first time
5 to talk about somebody's job in general
6 with a person's job title or their unique position in a company
7 with singular nouns to refer in general to all the members of a group
8 to talk about one of a number of things without being specific
9 with plural countable nouns to make general statements
10 with superlative adjectives and *first, last, only, same*
11 to refer to a thing or a person that has been previously mentioned, or that we already know about.

2 Complete the sentences with *the/a/an* or *0*.

1 .... last time I went for .... interview, I wore my blue suit.
2 We had .... quick meeting at break in .... staffroom.
3 .... teacher gave us .... project to work on during .... summer holidays.
4 .... creativity is .... important quality in people looking for work in .... television.
5 .... Internet has changed .... way we find information today.
6 Do you think I'll ever reach .... position of .... General Manager within this company?
7 .... companies need to provide easy access to .... workplace for .... disabled people.
8 Martin had .... job as .... waiter while he was waiting to go to .... university.

3 Circle the correct alternative.

1 Jack was sent to *the/0* prison for stealing money from the company he worked for.
2 Turn right and you'll find *the/0* school at the end of the road.
3 I was in *the/0* hospital for a week when I broke my leg.
4 I sometimes get lost in *the/0* hospital – there are so many floors and corridors.
5 My cousin's at *the/0* university in Paris and he's enjoying every minute of his course.
6 They are going to extend *the/0* prison because they need more accommodation for prisoners and staff.

4 Add *a/an* or *the* to the text where necessary.

PLANNING FOR THE FUTURE

Students who are looking for more information about possible careers and advice on what to do to make their ambitions reality will be interested in event we are holding over weekend of 14th–15th April, here at Garton College. Representatives of some of major UK companies will be on hand to talk to students about qualifications and job requirements and also to discuss recruitment procedures. There will be series of talks by experts about different career paths and wide range of job opportunities available to graduating students. You can book individual advice sessions with careers advisors, but please make sure that you book early as there will only be limited number of slots available. For more details on careers weekend, go to college website and click on 'careers at Garton'. Lot of hard work has gone into planning this event and we hope students will find it useful and interesting!

GRAMMAR CHALLENGE

5 Find and correct the 16 mistakes using articles in the email.

Hi Rob,

I finally heard result of an interview I had the last month. You remember? It was for a job of an assistant manager of my sector. Andy's an assistant manager at the moment, but he's been promoted so they held interviews for his replacement. It was, quite honestly, worst interview I'd ever done. I was a last to go in and I was really nervous by then. Questions were really easy, but I didn't answer at all well. Needless to say, I didn't get the job, but I'll try again next time. I shouldn't complain because I like my job and people I work with.

Anyway, how are you getting on at the university? Have you decided on the career yet? Make sure you get best advice possible! The unemployment is not an option!! Are you still sharing the house in Duke Street? I must come round to visit sometime. I've got couple of the DVDs you might like to watch.

Write soon,

Tom

1 Underline one word in each of the groups which does not collocate with the verb given. Then add two more words to each group.

1 GAIN: experience, qualification, opinion, insight, confidence

....

2 TAKE UP: hobby, staff, career

....

3 OVERCOME: fear, obstacle, problem, adversity, advantage

....

4 UNDERTAKE: study, direction, task, investigation

....

5 EMBARK ON: venture, project, revision

....

6 EXPERIENCE: pain, attention, situation

....

2 Circle the correct alternative.

1 The football coach's talk to the team before the match inspired a lot of *confidence/motivation*.
2 We'll have to weigh *over/up* the pros and cons of taking on a new project at the moment.
3 My brother used to *embark on/cause* a lot of trouble at school when he was younger.
4 If everyone were allowed to *speak/voice* their opinions, we'd be here all day!
5 A few weeks after the operation my mother *suffered/overcame* a setback and had to go back into hospital.
6 If you don't *take/pay* attention in lectures, you'll never pass the final exams.
7 If you don't agree, you should *talk/speak* your mind.
8 This job can be stressful and you have to be able to *stand/suffer* the pressure.

3 LISTENING 22 **Listen to a podcast about getting your first job. Match the speakers (1–3) to the jobs (a–c).**

1 Katie West	.....	a careers advisor
2 Sam Smith	.....	b lawyer
3 Marina Boyle	.....	c recruitment consultant

4 22 **Listen again. Answer the questions with no more than three words.**

1 How long did Katie spend trying to get her first job?

....

2 How did she get the job?

....

3 How does Sam say people feel when they don't get replies to their CVs?

....

4 What does he think you need to spend most time and effort on?

....

5 How long does it take Marina to decide if a CV is worth looking at?

....

6 What should you give to demonstrate your competencies?

....

7 Where did the company see Katie's profile?

....

8 What can you ask your work experience or internship supervisor to be?

....

VOCABULARY EXTENSION

5 Match the verbs to the nouns (1–10) to make collocations.

answer • break • demand • dismiss • miss
negotiate • outline • pose • promote • reach

1 .... a conclusion/a peak
2 .... a suggestion/a person
3 .... a query/the door
4 .... a contract/a promise
5 .... a question/a threat
6 .... a product/a person
7 .... an opportunity/ a (train/plane) connection
8 .... compensation/an explanation
9 .... a deal/ a contract
10 .... a plan/the difficulties

6 Use collocations from 5 to rewrite the sentences.

1 There was a chance to study in Spain as part of my course, but I applied too late.

....

2 If Tom says he will do something, he will definitely do it.

....

3 The worst unemployment figures were in 2015, then they declined.

....

4 The teacher wanted to know why we had handed in such poor work.

....

5 The authorities will not release a prisoner if they think he may still be dangerous to the public.

....

1 Match two sentences (a–f) to each definition (1–3).

a A CV **in which** the information has been adapted for the job is likely to get a second look.

b I can tell if someone has sent a generic CV, **in which case** it ends up in the bin.

c Sending hundreds of CVs, **most of which** never get read, is a waste of time.

d **At which point** I decided to revise my job-hunting strategy.

e We'll look at hundreds of profiles, **some of which** are a good fit.

f Last month the manager **for whom** I'd worked got in touch.

1 In more formal sentences, prepositions come before the relative pronoun. ...., ...

2 Prepositions come in some noun phrases which contain relative pronouns. ...., ...

3 Prepositions also appear in some adverbial phrases which contain relative pronouns. ...., ...

2 Rewrite these sentences to make them more formal.

1 The person I received the information from was Mr Peters.

....

2 This is the university that I studied at.

....

3 The office which I worked in last summer had no air conditioning.

....

4 The students who I worked with in July were all from Italy.

....

5 The languages I received top marks for at college were French and Russian.

....

6 I studied with a great teacher who I learnt a lot from.

....

3 Circle the correct alternative.

1 The restaurant might be closed, in which *case/point* we'll go to the pizzeria.

2 We drove until the car ran out of petrol, at which *reason/point* the car stopped.

3 Crime is a serious problem here, for which *reason/case* every effort should be made to reduce it.

4 The candidates, many of *whom/which* had travelled a long way, were all excellent.

5 I looked at the job adverts, some of *whom/which* I'd seen before.

4 Complete the sentences with these phrases.

many of whom • most of which • some of whom
the first of whom • the last of which

1 The series of books, ... has just come out, sold millions of copies.

2 The English students, ... went on an exchange programme last year, all did well in their language exams.

3 The book, ... was very technical, was very hard to follow. I understood hardly any of it.

4 The triplets, ... was born at 8.03 pm, were all healthy.

5 There are many international students on the music course, ... speak very little English. Of course, most of them speak excellent English.

GRAMMAR CHALLENGE

5 Find and correct ten mistakes.

Home | About | Articles |

The benefits of having a mentor

A mentor is ~~the~~ an experienced person who can help you with your job when you don't have much experience. A good mentor is someone from who you can learn a great deal. The office in that I worked was busy place and nobody had time to teach me so I found a mentor in another company. If I hadn't had my mentor, I didn't learn so much in the first year of my job.

Good mentors had already learnt to cope with the difficult aspects of the job and can demonstrate a behaviour you need to succeed. They will encourage you do your best and help you to succeed, too. They will act as a positive role model and show you what is require in your job.

This time next month my boss will be promote one person in the department and I think I have a good chance of getting the promotion – thanks to my mentor. I hope that in ten years' time I'll have got enough experience to help others, which point at I will become a mentor.

1 **Look at the photos. Complete the job descriptions and match them to the photos.**

A

B

C

D

E
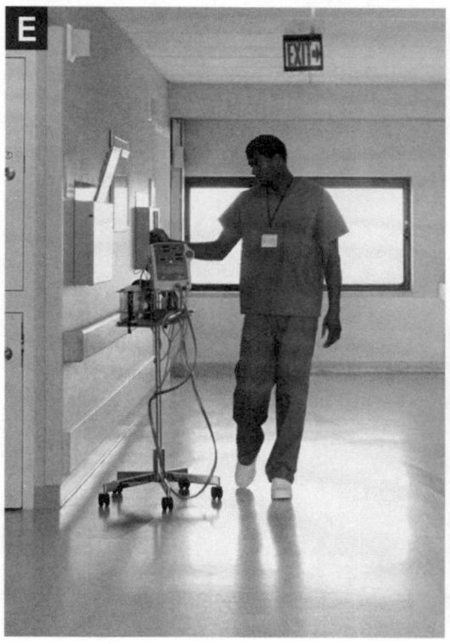

F

1 *Bus drivers* help people to get around in towns and cities. *D*
2 .... help people get better. ....
3 .... grow and produce food. ....
4 .... help produce a variety of goods. ....
5 .... help keep towns and cities clean. ....
6 .... help young people to learn. ....

2 LISTENING 23 **Listen to two students discussing the jobs A–F in 1. Put them in the order they are mentioned.**

1 .... 3 .... 5 ....
2 .... 4 .... 6 ....

3 23 **Listen again. Complete the sentences with one to three words.**

1 The girl says that factory workers make many products that are essential ....
2 The girl thinks bus drivers are important because not everyone has ....
3 The boy thinks that nurses are essential because .... is so important.
4 The girl says that teachers help prepare young people for ....
5 The girl says that in addition to food, farmers also provide other products such as ....
6 The girl points out that rubbish collectors do an important job and people forget that it is also ....

4 **Complete the phrases with these words.**

broadly • cases • extent • in
large • normally • of • on

1 By and ....
2 The majority ....
3 .... the whole
4 .... general
5 Usually/....................
6 In most ....
7 .... speaking
8 To a great ....

5 **Complete the sentences with one word.**

1 .... people would agree that having a heavy workload is very stressful.
2 To a great ...., I think long holidays are more important than salary.
3 .... and large, further training is important because it brings more job opportunities.
4 In most .... I think the physical conditions of the place where you work are important.
5 .... people want jobs where there is a chance of advancement and promotion.
6 .... speaking, I think it would be soul-destroying to be in a job where you had no possibility of influencing decisions.

6 **Read the exam task and then write the discussion. Try to use some expressions from 4.**

How important are these factors for job satisfaction?
- long holidays
- ability to influence decisions
- workload
- opportunities for promotion
- good physical work environment
- opportunities for further training

1 Correct the following useful expressions used in covering letters.

1 I write in response with your advertisement …

2 I am interest by the position to …

3 I could welcome the opportunity for work at your company

4 I believe I am good-suited in this job …

5 I have experience to working …

6 I consider myself being …

7 I am delighted attend an interview at your first convenience …

8 As request, I send my CV …

2 Read the advert. What is the job for? Look at the notes below and tick (✓) which information you would include in a covering letter.

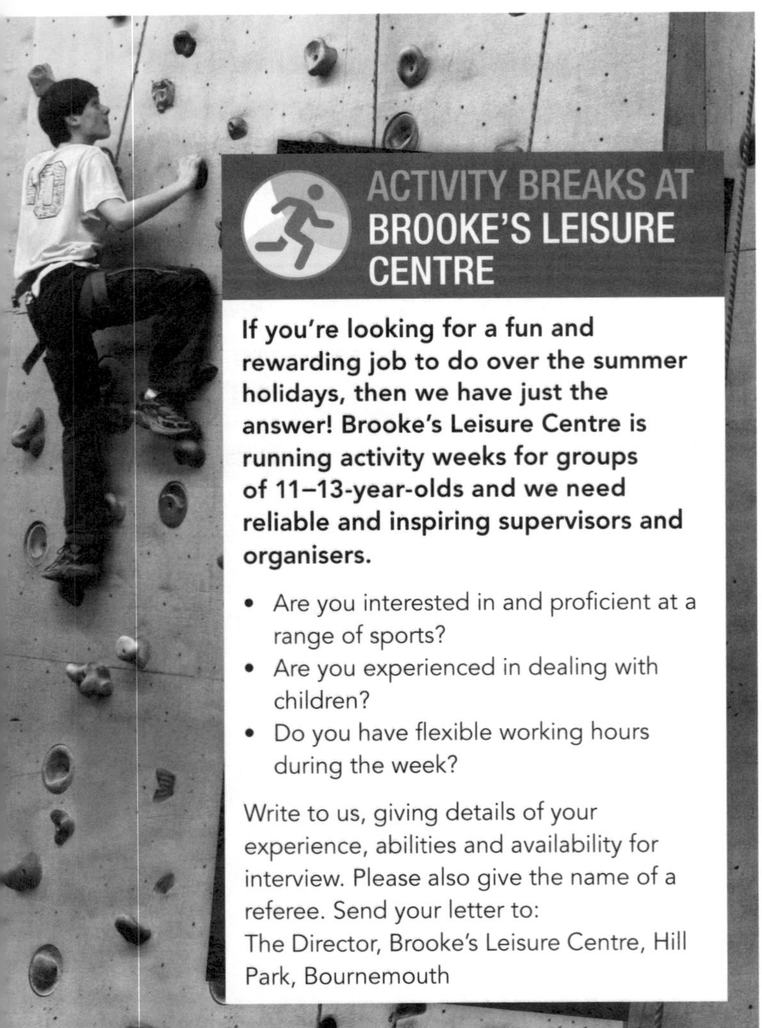

ACTIVITY BREAKS AT BROOKE'S LEISURE CENTRE

If you're looking for a fun and rewarding job to do over the summer holidays, then we have just the answer! Brooke's Leisure Centre is running activity weeks for groups of 11–13-year-olds and we need reliable and inspiring supervisors and organisers.

- Are you interested in and proficient at a range of sports?
- Are you experienced in dealing with children?
- Do you have flexible working hours during the week?

Write to us, giving details of your experience, abilities and availability for interview. Please also give the name of a referee. Send your letter to:
The Director, Brooke's Leisure Centre, Hill Park, Bournemouth

3 Order the paragraphs of a covering letter.

a give information about your character ☐
b give information so the company can continue further with the application ☐
c give basic information about yourself and why you are applying for the job ☐
d say why you are writing and which job you are applying for ☐
e state your relevant experience and/or relevant skills ☐

4 Make notes for each paragraph in a covering letter to apply for the job in 2.

- I am writing in response to …
- I am 18 years old and …
- I believe that I am …
- As for my personal qualities, …
- I would be delighted …

5 Write your covering letter. Use phrases from 1, your notes from 4 and the Writing bank in the Student's Book.

Remember to check:

- you have used correct paragraphing
- you have used formal language
- you have included your address, the address of the person/company you are writing to, the date
- you have laid out the letter correctly

1 ☐ sports centres are good places for kids to learn
2 ☐ excellent at swimming/riding, also good at cycling/tennis (won swimming competitions)
3 ☐ lots of babysitting experience. Big family – always organising younger siblings!
4 ☐ in future might study sport at university
5 ☐ time no problem, can be flexible
6 ☐ good exam results
7 ☐ very calm, can keep temper even in difficult situations
8 ☐ did first aid last month & have lifeguard certificate
9 ☐ did similar job last year – boss could be referee
10 ☐ available for interview

Grammar

1 Add articles to the email wherever necessary.

Hi Paul,

You know lot about IT and I need your advice! I'm thinking of buying new laptop for my mum's birthday. Old one she's using is really out of date. It's one I had when I was at school. When I went to university I got new laptop from my parents and I gave other one to Mum. I'm not sure what to get her. Liam's got tablet and he likes it a lot. Do you think laptops or tablets are better? And do you think it's good idea to buy it myself or go round shops with Mum so that she can choose one she wants? Let me know what you think.

Love, Maggie x

2 Rewrite the sentences using the words given.

1 The interviewer asked me a lot of questions but I couldn't answer any of them. **none**

....

2 It may be difficult to read my handwriting so do call me. **case**

....

3 I bought that e-reader for £50 second-hand. **that's**

....

4 I used to go to school with Peter and now he's a famous football player. **whom**

....

5 The supermarket I worked in has now closed down. **which**

....

3 Correct the mistakes. Some sentences may be correct.

1 I overheard Sarah to say that she's going to London next weekend.

....

2 Mr Brown is the man for who I used to work.

....

3 I think I'll study the course in engineering when I go to university.

....

4 Mark's face was red because he has been running for a long time.

....

5 The unemployed in this country receive benefits from the State.

....

6 Watching by her teammates, Lucy scored a goal just before the end of the match.

....

Vocabulary

1 Complete the sentences with the correct words.

1 I'm planning to e.................... on an English course this summer before I start university.

2 Some people prefer to s.................... an apprenticeship rather than continue academic study.

3 It's important for teachers to i.................... confidence in their students so that they have lots of drive to succeed.

4 When my mum had children she put her career on h...................., but now she's at the top of her profession.

5 Doing work experience is very useful for giving students an i.................... into working life.

2 Complete the sentences with the correct form of the verbs.

embark • gain • overcome • speak • stand
take • voice • weigh

1 Before .... on a career you really need to look carefully at the different professions and the qualifications you need to ....

2 When choosing between two jobs to apply for you must .... up the pros and cons carefully.

3 Whatever career path you choose, there will certainly be a range of obstacles that you will need to ....

4 In today's workplace people need to be able to .... a lot of pressure and .... responsibility early if they want to succeed. They should also know when it is advisable to .... their opinion and when not to .... their mind.

3 Choose the correct answers.

1 The police .... an investigation into the crime.
A underwent **B** undertook **C** understood

2 How are you settling .... to your new job?
A in **B** on **C** up

3 Mark is willing to try his .... at anything and he usually manages it!
A feet **B** hand **C** head

4 We're going to .... the property before we put in an offer.
A study **B** overlook **C** inspect

5 I'm going to .... my neck out and make a suggestion, though I know it won't be popular!
A stick **B** throw **C** push

6 I made the .... of my stay in Paris and visited lots of museums.
A more **B** much **C** most

7 I'm not interested in following in anybody else's .... I'll choose my own career.
A traces **B** ideas **C** footsteps

8 When does Simon .... his new position at the company?
A weigh up **B** take up **C** embark on

10 Found in translation

Reading

1 VOCABULARY **Complete the phrases in sentences 1–10 with the correct words. Then match them with the follow-up sentences (a–j).**

1 ☐ The student t.................. it literally when the teacher told him to pull his socks up.
2 ☐ John i.................. that my English wasn't very good.
3 ☐ I can never think of a w.................. remark to make when I need to.
4 ☐ I'm afraid I o.................. Maria unintentionally this morning.
5 ☐ I made a g.................. when I was speaking to Sarah yesterday.
6 ☐ I got the w.................. end of the stick about the concert.
7 ☐ It turned out that Jack and I were talking at c.................. purposes.
8 ☐ Your English has to be very good to be able to understand the n.................. .
9 ☐ I m.................. what the man said because I didn't know all the words.
10 ☐ There's something I find p.................. about English pronunciation.

a Sometimes meaning is conveyed by just a small change in tone.
b I asked her about her dog and apparently it died last week.
c I was asking him about the new TV series and he was talking about the book.
d He suggested that I go to some extra classes with him!
e Why on earth do 'enough' and 'photograph' have the same sound at the end?
f He looked down at his feet.
g I didn't understand him correctly.
h I said I liked her hair when it was longer.
i I thought it started at seven but it's at eight.
j It always occurs to me a few moments later.

2 **Read the three texts on page 85 quickly and match them with the headings (1–3).**

1 Babies have accents, too! ....
2 Could the language you speak affect your decisions? ....
3 The physical effects of language learning ....

3 **Read text A again and complete the summary. Use no more than two words for each answer.**

Scientists in Sweden did a study to find out the effects of **(a)** .... on the brain. They looked at two groups of students doing intensive courses in either languages or **(b)** .... MRI scans revealed that the language students' brains **(c)** .... in size whereas the brains of the control group hadn't **(d)** .... In the test group, the areas of the brain that increased in size varied according to students' **(e)** .... to learn language. Results of future studies should help teachers with **(f)** .... classes to suit students' learning styles.

4 **Read text B again and complete the table. Use no more than two words for each answer.**

	English	Chinese	Pormpuraaw
Type of language	Futured	Futureless	Kuuk Thaayorre
Features of language	Has many different **(a)**	Uses the **(b)** .... for past, present and future	Doesn't refer to objects **(c)** .... to us
Effect on people's behaviour	Tend to have less money and be in poorer **(d)** .... by retirement.	**(e)** .... more likely to save money in a year.	Know **(f)** .... which direction they are facing.

5 **Read text C again and decide if the statements are True (T), False (F) or the information is Not Mentioned (NM).**

1 The study looked at the sounds the babies made when they cried. T / F / NM
2 French babies cried with a greater variation in intonation than German babies. T / F / NM
3 Prosody is something children learn after birth. T / F / NM
4 The results showed that English speakers are more sarcastic than Cantonese speakers. T / F / NM
5 English speakers could only guess if Cantonese speakers were being sarcastic. T / F / NM

6 CRITICAL THINKING

How far do you think the language(s) you speak have affected your life in the ways described in the texts?

7 **Match the underlined words with the definitions.**

1 kept in the right direction ....
2 adapt to suit a purpose ....
3 saying the opposite of what you mean or speaking in a way intended to make someone feel stupid ....
4 connected with conscious mental processes ....
5 naturally, without thinking about something ....
6 pleasant to listen to ....

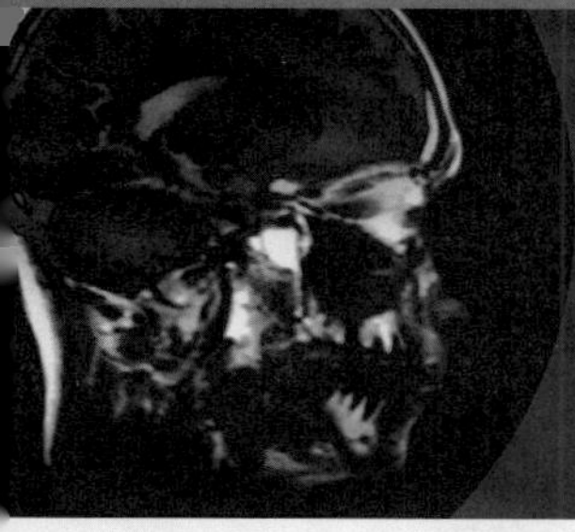

CHANGE YOUR LANGUAGE, CHANGE YOUR LIFE!

A Learning a foreign language can increase the size of your brain. This is what Swedish scientists discovered when they used MRI brain scans to see what happens inside the brain when someone learns a second language. In their experiment, two groups of students enrolled on intensive courses were analysed. The test group were learning new languages such as Arabic, Russian or Dari whereas the control group were studying in the fields of medicine and science. MRI scans after three months of intensive learning showed that parts of the brains of the language students had grown bigger whereas the brains of the other group remained unchanged.

> **"It seems that learning languages is a good way to keep the brain fit and healthy."**

Equally interesting was that different areas of the brain grew according to how easy the language learners found their studies. Students who had better language skills showed greater growth in the hippocampus and language learning areas of the cortex, while students who had some trouble learning showed greater growth in the motor region of the cerebral cortex. In other words, the areas of the brain in which changes take place are connected to how easy a person finds it to learn a language, and development varies according to performance.

It is unknown yet how much of an effect language learning over a longer period of time can have on brain size but it has been seen that being bilingual can delay or prevent brain diseases in later life. It seems that learning languages is a good way to keep the brain fit and healthy. And further studies are now being done to see how brain scanning can help detect which method of language learning is best for each individual, helping us tailor lessons to cognitive abilities. This should enable us to not only learn more quickly and easily but also hopefully enjoy learning more, too.

B If you are Chinese, you are likely to have more money in later life than if you are English. Why? Because of grammar! Chinese is one of a number of 'futureless languages' – it uses the same phrases to describe events in the past, present and future, unlike the 'futured' languages such as English, which have different verb tenses. Economist Keith Chen wanted to know if this affects our economic decisions. To do this, he looked at the behaviour of speakers of 'futured' and 'futureless' languages.

> **"Futureless language speakers are 30% more likely to save money in any given year than futured language speakers."**

After analysing the data, Chen discovered that futureless language speakers are 30% more likely to save money in any given year than futured language speakers. Over a lifetime, this could add up to futureless language speakers having saved 25% more for retirement than futured language speakers, which is a significant difference. They also tend to be healthier as they make better decisions related to their health. Chen believes that this difference is due to the fact that futureless language speakers are more motivated to save and prepare for the future because the words they use to talk about the present and future are the same, so the future seems more immediate. When we speak about the future in a different tense, it feels more distant and so we are less motivated to save money and be healthy now in order to be more comfortable in later life.

Another example of how language can affect behaviour is when we talk about directions. Whereas in English we talk about a place or object being on the 'left' or 'right' in relation to us, about a third of the world's languages only refer to places and things as being 'northeast' or 'southwest'. According to one linguistic expert, speakers of languages like this, such as some Australian Aboriginal communities, like the Pormpuraaw, who speak Kuuk Thaayorre, are far better at staying oriented and keeping track of where they are, even in unfamiliar landscapes. Some even know instinctively which direction they are facing. It's certainly something to think about next time you get lost!

C Can babies cry with different accents? According to new research, yes! We all have accents in our own language, depending on what country we are from and even which part of the country we come from, and when we learn a foreign language, most of us speak with a foreign accent. But it was thought that people only acquired accents when they learnt to speak. Now, a study of 60 French and German babies has shown that babies cry with an 'accent'.

It was the first study to demonstrate that babies pick up their mother's speech patterns before they are born and this influences the way they cry. French babies generally cried with a more melodious rising intonation, like the intonation often used by French speakers, and German babies had a harsher cry with falling intonation, similar to most German speakers. This is because every language has a unique set of intonations, called the prosody. The research shows that babies learn this prosody even before birth, making it easier for them to learn their native language.

> **"Babies cry with an 'accent'."**

Prosody means we can detect things like sarcasm because we pick up on the specific intonation that is used to be sarcastic. Interestingly, sarcasm sounds completely different in different languages. A series of three studies of English and Cantonese speakers showed that in English people spoke more slowly, with a wider range of intonation when they were being sarcastic, while in Cantonese people spoke faster and with a narrower range of intonation. While speakers could easily identify sarcasm in their own language they could only guess if speakers of the other language were being sarcastic.

1 Complete the rules with *infinitive* or *gerund*.

1 After *too, enough, the first* and *the last* we use the ....

2 As the subject or object of a sentence we use the ....

3 After prepositions we use the ....

4 Immediately after adjectives we use the ....

5 After verbs of liking or disliking such as *enjoy, hate, can't stand* we use the ....

6 After certain noun phrases such as *it's no good* or *have difficulty with* we use the ....

7 To explain purpose or use we use the ....

8 After indefinite pronouns (e.g. *someone, something*) we use the ....

2 Match the example sentences (a–h) with the rules (1–8) in 1.

a Babies learn this prosody even before birth, which makes it easier **to learn** their native language. ....

b **To do** this, he looked at the behaviour of speakers of different types of languages. ....

c After **analysing** the data, Chen discovered futureless language speakers are more likely to save money. ....

d **Learning** a foreign language can increase the size of your brain. ....

e This should enable us to enjoy **learning** languages more, too. ....

f It was the first study **to demonstrate** that babies pick up their mother's speech patterns before they are born. ....

g It's certainly something **to think about** next time you get lost! ....

h Students who had trouble **learning** showed greater growth in the motor region. ....

3 Circle the correct alternative.

1 To understand/Understanding English idioms is one of the biggest problems I have.

2 After cause/causing a huge amount of damage along the shore, the storm moved inland.

3 It was revision, so the exercise was easy to do/doing.

4 When the teacher asked for volunteers, Grace was the first to put/putting up her hand.

5 The reason I went to the library was to get/getting out a book on the history of languages.

6 It's no good to ask/asking Fred for help with this exercise!

7 Agnieska enjoys to watch/watching films in English. It helps her to improve/improving her English.

8 My brother can't stand to get/getting up early at the weekend.

4 Complete the dialogue with the correct form of the verbs given.

A: I'm going to America this summer **(a)** .... (improve) my English. I'm looking forward to **(b)** .... (go), but I'm worried about the accent. I've never had an American teacher and **(c)** .... (understand) the accent is hard for me. I'm worried I'll have problems **(d)** .... (follow) what people say.

B: It's worth **(e)** .... (watch) some American films before you go **(f)** .... (get) used to the accent.

A: I suppose it is important **(g)** .... (practise) now. I hadn't thought of that.

B: And get a translation app on your phone **(h)** .... (look up) words you don't know. They're easy enough **(i)** .... (download) and most of them are free.

A: That's a good idea. Thanks!

5 Complete the table with the verbs.

~~admit~~ • apologise for • arrange • ask • carry on
consider • decide • deny • expect • feel like
hope • include • inspire • like • persuade
practise • remind • risk • seem

Verb + gerund	Verb + infinitive
admit	

GRAMMAR CHALLENGE

6 Find and correct the nine mistakes in the advert.

Study with us!

Do you need improving your English for work or study?
Perhaps you want to travel and use English interacting with the people you meet. We can help you achieving your ideal level. Peers Language School has an excellent reputation for to help students from all over the world improving their language skills. We run courses throughout the year and we can arrange for you staying with a local family. You can choose coming in the summer and enjoy all the seaside attractions that the wonderful town of Eastbourne has offering. It's also worth to come in the winter months when the classes are smaller.

1 Choose the correct answers.

1 The teacher ………… out that the pronunciation of words like 'bath' is different around the UK.
A indicated B pointed C showed

2 Beth brought ………… the subject of the museum trip.
A in B out C up

3 I hate it when the teacher talks ………… to us. We're not kids!
A over B down C out

4 The line was bad and I couldn't ………… out what Rob was asking me to do.
A make B take C see

5 Let's turn ………… the subject of money. Now, who is going to be paying for this?
A to B at C for

6 Do I have to spell it …………? I said I didn't want to go!
A up B on C out

7 During the debate quite a few people ………… out in favour of lowering the age for voting.
A spoke B talked C said

8 Sometimes I can't get ………… to my sister. She's in her own little world.
A over B across C through

9 Ed and I were having a conversation when Daniel cut ………….
A across B in C through

10 The teacher didn't pick up ………… the fact that I hadn't done the homework.
A in B over C on

2 Rewrite the second sentence so that it has a similar meaning to the first, using the word given. Do not change the word.

1 It was difficult for me to understand exactly what Mark was saying. **make**

…………………………………………

2 About 50% of the people there said that they supported our idea. **favour**

…………………………………………

3 I wasn't aware of Jodie's absence in class this morning. **pick**

…………………………………………

4 Making people understand what you mean is sometimes not that easy! **get**

…………………………………………

5 I hate it when people interrupt my conversations. **in**

…………………………………………

3 LISTENING 24 Are the statements True (T), False (F) or Not Mentioned (NM)? Guess the answers. Listen to a podcast about languages and check.

1 When you can't speak a language it always sounds like nonsense. T/F/NM
2 Italian sounds melodious to most people. T/F/NM
3 German only sounds harsh to people in southern Europe. T/F/NM
4 Thai and Mandarin Chinese are both tonal languages. T/F/NM
5 It is possible to make a judgement about which languages are beautiful. T/F/NM

4 24 Listen again and complete the summary. Use a maximum of three words or numbers but use the words you hear. You can listen twice.

Some languages such as French, Italian and Spanish are often described as beautiful, **(a)** ………… . Others are described as harsh. Why?

The videos on YouTube show you can identify a language even when it is spoken in gibberish and know if it **(b)** ………… to you or not. Languages with sounds that don't exist in your own language usually sound **(c)** ………… . Italian is probably considered a beautiful language because it has few sounds that are **(d)** ………… other European languages.

A language can also be attractive if we value it. English is a valued language because apart from native speakers, **(e)** ………… other people speak it. Mandarin Chinese is becoming more popular because China is an area of **(f)** ………… .

In sociolinguistics, the study of the **(g)** ………… between language and society, there is a theory that attractiveness of a language may depend on how positively we view the **(h)** ………… . This theory is difficult to prove because it is hard to distinguish between **(i)** ………… because people are influenced by their own experiences.

Sociolinguists have also called attention to the fact that no language is better than any other and they all play an important **(j)** ………… in communication.

Learning another language can **(k)** ………… of how attractive it is, when strange sounds become more familiar. After studying a new language for just a few months, the presenter started to **(l)** ………… more.

VOCABULARY EXTENSION

5 Complete the phrasal verbs in italics with the correct word.

back • by • in • through • up

1 If you're having problems with someone, it's best to *talk* things ………… with them.
2 You've *come* ………… *with* some excellent ideas today.
3 It was an interesting talk on English literature but there was a lot to *take* ………… .
4 Thanks for your email. I'll *get* ………… *to* you with the answers to your queries as soon as I can.
5 I've got a couple of ideas to *run* ………… you, if you've got a moment?

1 Complete the rules with these words.

doesn't make • however • makes • whenever

1 We use ...., *whichever, whoever,* etc. when it .... a difference *who, when, which,* etc.

2 We use .... + adjective/adverb when it .... a difference how much you do something or how big/small/difficult something is.

2 Match the examples (a–c) to the rules (1–2) above.

a **Whoever** you ask will probably find these languages attractive too.

b **However** hard we try not to let our personal experiences affect our judgement, it's inevitable that they do.

c **Whenever** I hear Arabic now, I find it beautiful and melodious.

3 Choose the correct answers.

1 It's a great language school, ... your needs, they can help you.
A whenever **B** whatever **C** however

2 Sara couldn't solve the problem .... hard she tried.
A whoever **B** whenever **C** however

3 There are lots of good travel books. I'm sure .... you choose will be good.
A whichever **B** whatever **C** whenever

4 The auditions are today. .... happens, I'm glad I decided to try.
A Whatever **B** However **C** Wherever

5 .... I hear that song, I think of you.
A Whatever **B** Whenever **C** However

6 .... Henry went, he took his dogs with him.
A Whoever **B** However **C** Wherever

4 Complete the dialogue with the correct word ending in *-ever*.

A: So, you're off on your exchange visit to England at the weekend. You'll love it!

B: Yeah – I'm really looking forward to it. Any tips?

A: Well, **(a)** .... you do – don't forget to take a present for your host family with you. They'll appreciate that.

B: I'll remember that.

A: And **(b)** .... you speak to, ask them to speak slowly!

B: OK!

A: You'll find really kind people **(c)** .... you go in England. I made some really good friends there. Oh, and the weather. Remember, **(d)** .... sunny it is in the morning, take your umbrella, because you never know what it's going to be like later!

B: That's good advice. What about food?

A: Well, I can guarantee that **(e)** .... restaurant you go into in England – you can order chips. And **(f)** .... you go you'll find fast food restaurants – just like here. One piece of advice – **(g)** .... someone offers you a coffee, say you'd like a strong one, because the coffee is usually quite weak. Oh, and **(h)** .... happens, be polite. The English language is full of polite phrases because they use them a lot!

B: Thanks!

GRAMMAR CHALLENGE

5 Find and correct the mistakes in the sentences. Some sentences are correct.

1 It was interesting see that the results of the survey reflected my predictions.
....

2 It's a plant that grows whatever there's a hot climate.
....

3 The first person answering the question correctly will get a prize.
....

4 By the time you read this, I'll be sitting on the beach and enjoying the view.
....

5 We're determined having a great holiday however much it costs.
....

6 If you could choose to live anywhere in the world, where do you go?
....

7 I trust James completely, so I'd do whichever he asked me to do.
....

8 There's no point in arguing. Whatever you say, Chris won't listen.
....

1 Look at the photo and answer the questions.

1 Who do you think the people are?

....

2 What subject might the children be learning?

....

3 What do you think the main difficulties might be?

....

4 How do you think they might deal with the difficulties?

....

2 LISTENING ▶ 25 **Read the speaking task below. Listen to a student doing the task about her learning experience. Does she mention any of your ideas in 1?**

> Talk about the main difficulties you had when you started learning English. You should say:
> - what the main difficulties have been
> - why you think these were problematic for you
> - how you dealt with the difficulties
> - what you might do differently if you could go back and start again

3 ▶ 25 **Listen again. Are the sentences True (T) or False (F)?**

1 She started learning English when she was six years old. T/F
2 She remembers the colour her English teacher's clothes often were. T/F
3 She had a lot of problems because the classes weren't fun. T/F
4 She doesn't use a dictionary because she prefers to learn spelling another way. T/F
5 Her teacher helped her with her pronunciation. T/F
6 She wouldn't do anything different if she could go back and start again. T/F

4 Complete the highlighted phrases with the correct words.

1 **I** .... **to remember that** my first English teacher liked wearing red clothes.

2 **I have a** .... **memory of** being asked to pretend I was a banana in an English game.

3 **The most** .... **memory I have** is of jumping up and down to the rhythm of an English chant.

4 **What** .... **me was** how difficult it was to spell English words.

5 **What** .... **in my mind is** that I could never pronounce 'the' correctly and the teacher kept making me practise it.

5 Read the task below and write your answer. Remember to use phrases from the Speaking bank in the Student's Book.

> Talk about what you think is the best way to learn another language. You should say:
> - why you think it is the best way
> - how it is better than other methods of learning languages
> - what you would change about the way you learnt a language

1 Read the memo to student representatives and answer the questions.

We are considering organising an English camp in the summer holidays to encourage students to develop their proficiency in English. We wondered if you could send a proposal with ideas on how to make the camp a success and financially attractive to as many students as possible, and also where to hold it.

Thanks,

P. Blanco

Head of English

1 Who is it from?

2 What three areas of information should the proposal cover?

2 Complete the expressions in the table with these words.

aim • also • balance • could • dispute light • outlines • suggest • sum relates • well

Introduction
The .... of this proposal is to …
This proposal .... to …
This proposal describes/.................... …
Outlining the situation
In the .... of students' comments, …
It is beyond .... that …
Suggestions
We .... …
… should …
I/We .... that …
Adding information
We could .... …
… as .... as …
Conclusions
To .... up,
On ...., we are of the opinion that …

3 Read the proposal and add expressions to the table in 2.

4 Read the proposal again and answer the questions.

1 Does it cover all the areas asked for in the memo in 1?

2 Is it clear and organised? How?

3 Find four examples of the passive. Why is it used?

PROPOSAL TO ORGANISE AN ENGLISH CAMP IN THE SUMMER HOLIDAYS

Introduction

This proposal looks at ways to organise an English camp in the summer holidays, make it a success and keep the costs down to attract as many students as possible. The school currently has 700 students and we estimate that around two hundred would be interested in attending the camp. We believe it would be a valuable and beneficial extracurricular event.

1 Activities

Having spoken to students in every class, it is clear from their comments that the English camp has to offer a variety of activities and not just English classes. The activities that would be popular include doing a variety of sports and cultural activities. We propose that the camp also offer quiz competitions, films in English and a weekly talent show where students perform in English. We could also offer specialities such as theatre and film-making.

2 Length of the camp

With regard to the length of the camp, the general view is that it should be three weeks long. Students would have the option of attending for one, two or three weeks. This means that students who might not be able to go to longer summer camps have the possibility of going for at least a week. Additionally, we could organise a sponsored walk so students can raise funds.

3 Location

If the camp is held in this country, this would keep the costs down. Also worth mentioning is the fact that summer camps in a village only 80 km away have previously been organised by another local school. Perhaps this site could be used as a venue.

4 Conclusions

In conclusion, we would say that a summer camp would be of interest to a high number of students. To attract participation, we propose that the organisers include an appealing number of fun activities in addition to English classes. We also recommend that students be offered the possibility of attending for between one and three weeks and organising an event to help them raise funds to pay for the camp. Finally, having the camp in a nearby location would also help to keep the costs down.

5 Read the memo from a school principal to student representatives. Make notes for a proposal following the paragraph plan.

From: The Principal

To: Student Representatives

We are considering organising a school trip to London. We wondered if you could send a proposal with ideas to make the trip a success and help attract participants, and suggest when to organise it for.

Thanks,

S. Harris

Introduction

1 Making the trip a success

2 Attracting participants

3 Organisation

4 Conclusions

6 Write your proposal. Use the phrases from 2, your notes from 5 and the Writing bank in the Student's Book.

Remember to check:

- you have used correct paragraphing
- you have used formal language

Grammar

1 Circle the correct alternative.

1 I have difficulty to translate/translating English to Polish.
2 I'm phoning to ask/asking if you'd like to come round after dinner.
3 To do/Doing overtime isn't a problem for me at all.
4 Can you put those plastic bottles into the bag for to recycle/recycling please?
5 It's definitely worth to apply/applying for the holiday job at the summer camp.
6 If I do a Saturday job it will mean to get/getting up really early.
7 I must find someone to help/helping me fix this virus on my computer.
8 I hate to fill/filling in application forms – it's so boring.

2 Complete the sentences with the correct words ending in -ever.

1 .... my French friend comes to England she brings some cheese for my parents.
2 It's important to take on new challenges .... difficult they may be.
3 .... was on the computer last didn't close it down properly.
4 .... I say to Annie at the moment it's the wrong thing!
5 Penny takes her laptop with her .... she goes.
6 You can borrow .... book you want to read as long as you return it when you finish.

3 Complete the message with one suitable word in each gap. Contractions count as one word.

Hi Paul,

Not sure what time you're due home, but **(a)** .... time you get back, could you do **(b)** .... few things for me?

- Put the chicken in the oven and don't **(c)** .... to turn it on! I've **(d)** .... peeled the potatoes but **(e)** .... you boil them for me?
- Put the washing from the machine outside to dry – **(f)** .... it's raining.
- The dog **(g)** .... have been inside **(h)** .... lunchtime, so please let him out into the garden.
- Mike **(i)** .... have fixed the car and returned it. If he **(j)** ...., could you ring him and remind him **(k)** .... bring it round?

Thanks!

Mum xx

Vocabulary

1 Complete the sentences.

1 In the end it turned out that Brad and I had been talking at cross ....
2 Helen tried to explain how to work out the tax, but I still .... it very puzzling.
3 At the party Mark made a .... remark that made everyone laugh because it was so funny!
4 I always get the wrong .... of the stick when someone explains something to me in another language.
5 It's hard to understand .... in another language because the differences are so slight.

2 Choose the correct answers.

1 The examiner picked .... on a few of my problems with vocabulary.
A up **B** down **C** off
2 Some bosses talk .... to new employees and that's not a good thing.
A over **B** on **C** down
3 Jane was speaking so quickly I couldn't make .... what she was saying.
A off **B** out **C** up
4 If I have a problem at work I usually turn .... my immediate boss who is very understanding and helpful.
A to **B** at **C** for
5 In my assessment interview, my boss brought .... the fact that I'd been absent quite a lot last year.
A in **B** up **C** over
6 May I point .... that you've had a week to research this topic!
A to **B** out **C** in

3 Circle the correct alternative.

1 There was a heart-finishing/stopping chase in the film.
2 I once made a terrible remark/gaffe when I was speaking to our managing director at the company dinner. I mistook him for a new colleague!
3 I recently read an eye-opening/grabbing article about the celebrity's life.
4 Scott spoke/talked out in favour of the idea.
5 I listened carefully but I couldn't make up/out what he was saying.
6 My brother carried/served a two-year apprenticeship before becoming a mechanic.
7 My parents suffered a few outbreaks/setbacks when they first tried to buy a house in Spain.
8 I unintentionally offended/misinterpreted Sally when I asked how old she was.

Reading

1 Read the article and complete the summary with words from the text. Use no more than two words in each answer.

It's slang for attractive, and begins with 'p'.

CAN YOU PASS THE YOUTH TEST?

Here is a simple test, for which there is a one-word answer. What word is slang for attractive, and begins with 'p'? If you're a British teenager, then you will know the answer is *peng*. If you're older or not from the UK, it's likely you didn't know the answer.

How can this one small word be so baffling for anyone over the age of 20 and yet so commonplace for anyone under? According to Jonnie Robinson, the sociolinguistics curator at the British Library, 'It doesn't matter where the teenagers come from,' Robinson said. 'Yesterday I had an all-female, all-white group of girls from Manchester Grammar School. They all said "peng". It's all classes, regions, everywhere.' A lot of the students also said 'well peng', which, Robinson says, shows how quickly Jamaican patois has been absorbed into contemporary British speech. When asked the question, British adults might say 'pretty', which isn't even slang. The word you choose says something very revealing about the future of the English language and identity.

Language purists used to complain that the English language was being changed by Americans. Transatlantic speech – as featured in most mainstream films, music and television – was the biggest influence on British English. But that is no longer true. The vocabulary teenagers in the UK use and even the way they speak is being transformed by the languages they hear around them.

Of course teenagers have always used slang, but what Robinson's Evolving English project at the British Library has revealed is more than that: a generational divide, with young people shaping the future of English in unexpected ways. It turns out that Americans are, contrary to reputation, preserving the old-fashioned way of speaking English. It's modern Britons who are the radical ones, responding not to American English, but to the English spoken by Caribbean and Asian immigrants.

There are about 359 million native English speakers, but 850 million speak it as a second language. The fact that native speakers are now the minority may come as a surprise, and to chart the effect on the English language, Robinson has collected as many voices speaking today's English as he can as part of the project.

Another example of a changing word is 'controversy'. If you say it aloud, where does the stress fall? The English dictionary states that the only way to say it is to put the stress on the first syllable. And according to the Evolving English project, this is the way that Americans say it. But in the UK, this way is dying out: 'controversy' is a mark of youth. 'This change is happening only in the UK,' Robinson says. The same applies to 'harrass', or 'applicable'. Older people would say 'harass' and 'applicable'. Young people have changed the pronunciation to 'harass' and 'applicable'. Older British people often get very annoyed by this transformation and tend to blame the Americans for it. But it's the British changing, not the Americans.

Though Britons do sometimes use American vocabulary, it is only in certain contexts, for example, ordering a burger and fries in a fast-food restaurant because that's what's on the menu. But nobody talks to their friends entirely in American English just because they've seen it in films. According to Robinson, what is most important is face-to-face contact. And because at any British secondary school there will be more Asian-English or Jamaican-English speakers than Americans, that is the direction in which English is changing.

Eventually, most sociolinguists believe, sheer weight of numbers will force native English speakers to change to the way English-as-a-second-language speakers are speaking. There are between 200 and 300 languages spoken in London alone. For example, 'a few pieces of advice' may be lost in favour of what some Chinese-English speakers call 'advices'. It's more efficient that way. But don't worry – it's the future, and it's the way it has always been.

British SLANG

English is changing because **(a)** .... who live in today's multicultural society are using it in a different way. For example, the word *peng* is now being used to mean **(b)** '....................'. This is an example of current **(c)** .... Older people probably **(d)** .... it. According to Jonnie Robinson, words like *peng* are known to teenagers from different social backgrounds and **(e)** .... of the UK.

The British Library project shows that Americans are continuing to speak a more **(f)** .... kind of English. Young British people, however, are being influenced by the English spoken by **(g)** .... from the Caribbean and Asia. This is not surprising when you consider that there are now far more speakers of English as a second language than **(h)** .... Another example of changing language is the pronunciation of the word 'controversy', which young people now pronounce with the stress on the **(i)** ....

Though Britons do use American English vocabulary in certain situations, it seems that **(j)** .... has more influence on the way the language changes. Since there are now a lot of **(k)** .... students who are Asian-English and Jamaican-English speakers, this is having a bigger impact on British English than American English. Experts predict that in the **(l)** .... everyone in the country will speak a different kind of English as a result of English-as-a-second-language speakers.

Use of English

2 Read the text and choose the correct answers.

Emailing has overtaken letter-writing as **(1)** .... most common form of communication in the world. However, it is important **(2)** .... that there are some basic rules when it comes to writing emails. **(3)** .... you do, don't write an email quickly and send it off without checking what you've written. **(4)** .... spelling and grammar isn't the only thing you should do – you should also check that the language is an appropriate level of formality for the person to **(5)** .... you are writing. If you want to **(6)** .... to your reader then make sure the message is clear. While it's OK to **(7)** .... your mind in face-to-face communication, you have to be extremely careful in an email because you run the risk of **(8)** .... the other person unintentionally. Remember, when we speak we convey a lot of **(9)** .... with our body language: this is why written language is more open to misinterpretation. Finally, don't use only **(10)** .... capital letters, because that's equivalent to shouting, or only lowercase, as it looks lazy.

	A	B	C
1	the	a	*0*
2	remembering	remember	to remember
3	However	Whichever	Whatever
4	Look at	Looking at	To look at
5	who	that	whom
6	get by	get through	get on
7	tell	speak	say
8	offend	to offend	offending
9	nuances	gaffes	purposes
10	*0*	the	a

Listening

3 LISTENING 26 Listen to a podcast about keeping secrets and answer the questions. Write no more than three words for each answer.

1 How many groups took part in the research?

....

2 What kind of secrets did the first group have to keep?

....

3 What was in the picture that the participants were shown?

....

4 Which group thought the hill was more difficult to climb?

....

5 What kind of tasks seem harder when you spend a lot of time thinking about a worrying secret?

....

6 What did the study in 2014 suggest people do about worrying secrets?

....

Writing

4 Choose one of these two writing tasks. Write between 120 and 180 words.

1 You have seen the following advert and decide to apply. Write your letter of application.

Children's Activity Leaders

We have several vacancies for Children's Activity Leaders at this year's Edinburgh International Book Festival. Duties include preparing and distributing materials, supervising children and leading them in various book-related activities.

Good level of English essential as well as experience of working with children and an interest in children's literature.

Good pay and accommodation provided.

Please send CV and a covering letter to:
Recruitments, Edinburgh Book Festival, PO Box 14689, Edinburgh, EH7 2BD

2 Read the memo by the school principal. Then write a proposal.

We are considering setting up an after-school group for students who are interested in finding out more about career options. We would like to hear whether students would be interested and to know if you have any suggestions. Some possibilities include:

- getting speakers from local businesses
- workshops on writing CVs and covering letters
- workshops on assessing strengths and weaknesses

➪ writing career plans?
➪ preparing for interviews?
➪ filling in application forms?
➪ workshops on doing apprenticeships?

! COMMON MISTAKES

5 Correct the mistakes in the sentences.

1 The manager is the person to who I spoke.
2 I usually buy electronic goods at a local shop because people who work there are very helpful.
3 It was difficult to make up what Karen was saying because the restaurant was very noisy.
4 I spent two months travelling in America for to improve my level of English.
5 It's no use ask Jonas to help you, he's too busy.
6 I have a lot of things for what to be grateful.
7 It's impossible to learn all the words in a language, whatever long you spend studying it.
8 It's easy understanding them because they speak slowly and clearly.
9 In my family, I'm usually the first person getting home in the evening.
10 This is the school in that I studied – I had a lot of good teachers there.

Academic Writing

PURPOSE AND PLANNING

- The first step to writing academically is to clearly define the purpose of the writing.
- Think about the audience or reader and always answer the question that has been set.
- When you have a clear idea of what is required, make a plan. This will help you produce a clear, coherent and well-structured assignment. Refer back to your plan as you are writing and stay focused on answering the question.
- Use planning techniques that suit you, e.g. brainstorming, mind-maps, lists or a mixture of these.

STRUCTURE AND PARAGRAPHING

- The structure of a piece of writing will be determined by the text type (essay, report etc.). However, most writing follows the same overall structure: beginning/middle/end or introduction/main body/conclusion.
- Think about the structure of each main paragraph. Start with your main point before providing details, evidence and examples. A logical order makes it easier for the reader to follow.

FORMAL LANGUAGE

- In academic writing you are expected to use formal language and not colloquial or informal language.
- Do not use contractions like *don't, can't* or *mustn't*.
- If you want to sound more formal and objective use the passive and avoid personal pronouns. For example, instead of *We think a new gym is the best solution*, write *A new gym is considered to be the best solution*.
- However, the active voice can be direct and easier to read than the passive, so be careful to choose the most appropriate form.

EDITING AND PROOFREADING

- **Editing** focuses on the content of the text. When editing, check that the text flows logically, is coherent and concise, has a consistent tone, has a clear purpose and makes sense as a whole.
- **Proofreading** focuses on noticing and correcting errors in spelling, grammar and punctuation. Make sure that you proofread every piece of work carefully before you submit it to your teacher. Sometimes it can help to ask a classmate or friend to proofread for you.

REFERENCING

- Sometimes it is necessary to add references to your work to demonstrate how widely the subject has been researched.
- The referencing style used depends on the institution and subject, but as a general rule a reference should include:
  - title of chapter
  - journal article or web page (if appropriate)
  - title of publication (book, journal, website) in *italics*
  - edition or volume (if appropriate)
  - place of publication
  - publisher
- Make sure that you do not use anyone else's work or ideas without adding the source to your work. This is called plagiarism and could get you into serious trouble.

Reading

SKIMMING AND SCANNING

- **Skim** texts quickly for general understanding or to get the main ideas. Read the beginning and focus briefly on the first lines (topic sentences) of the other paragraphs.
- Skimming is useful when reading non-fiction texts especially when you have a large amount of material to cover, e.g. reading an online news website to get the main points of the news but not the details.
- **Scan** texts when looking for specific facts or information. Identify your purpose for looking for the specific information, locate the key words you are looking for, and then read the relevant sections. Remember when you scan that your aim is to find specific pieces of information. Becoming familiar with how different reference materials are structured will help you scan effectively, so practise using dictionaries, the index of books and websites, etc.
- In reading exams, use skimming and scanning in each task to firstly get a general idea of the text and then look quickly for the information you need.

READING TO UNDERSTAND A SUBJECT

- **Preview** the material by skimming the major headings and sub-headings of the text, book or syllabus.
- **Question**. Formulate questions about the material.
- **Read** actively in order to answer your own questions.
- **Summarise** the material using notes, spider diagrams and/or mnemonics.
- **Test** yourself by trying to remember the key ideas. Review the material that has been forgotten.

Speaking

FLUENCY AND ACCURACY

- To speak well you will need to improve both fluency and accuracy.
- **To improve fluency,** take advantage of all opportunities to speak English in the classroom and focus on getting your message across. It is natural to hesitate, rephrase (*what I mean is…*) and repeat yourself using different words. Just try to keep talking.
- Outside the classroom, use conversation exchange websites or practise with a friend. Watch TV series and films in English and try to repeat phrases as you hear them.
- **To improve accuracy**, listen to yourself as you are speaking and try to self-correct. If your teacher corrects you, write down the mistake and the correction. Try to use the corrected version as soon as possible. You can also record yourself speaking on mobile devices. Play the recording back to make a note of any errors and good language to use again.

HESITATION DEVICES

- When speaking, if you need time to think you can use sounds like *umm, err* and *ah*. You can also use the following 'fillers':
  - *Let me see …* or *Let me think …* This gives you time to think.
  - *That's a good/interesting question …* This should only be used when the question is interesting or unusual, however.
  - *To be honest …* This can be used when you are giving unexpected information, e.g. *What is your favourite sport? To be honest, I don't like sport.*

EXTENDING YOUR SPEECH

- Extend your speech by giving examples. Examples could be about you, people you know, or people in general.
- Other examples could contrast the present with past or future time, e.g. *What are you studying? Well, at the moment I am studying English but next year I hope to be studying Law at university.*

Listening

EXAMS

- **Before listening:** Use all available time to read the introduction to the task, read the questions and think about the topic. Underline the key ideas in questions to help you focus on what you are listening for.
- **While listening:** Keep your eyes on the question paper. If you miss an answer or if there is a section that you do not understand, relax, keep focused on the question and keep listening. Use the second listening to check your answers and listen out for things you missed the first time.

LECTURES

- **Before the lecture:** Bring something to write with and a notebook. Arrive early and sit where you can concentrate best. If you know the title of the lecture, do some reading before and think about what you would like to learn.
- **During the lecture:** Listen actively by thinking about what you are hearing. What questions are asked? Do you agree with what is being said? Take notes (see NOTE TAKING).
- **After the lecture:** Review lecture notes as soon as possible after the lecture. If possible, compare notes with another student to fill in any gaps in your notes. File your notes appropriately and do any follow-up reading.

NOTE TAKING

- Do not try to write every word you hear. Try to note the main points, plus any supporting facts and examples.
- Some students use abbreviations and colour coding, others use word maps and spider diagrams. Develop a system that works for you.

REFLECTION

- At the end of the year, reflect on what you have studied, learnt and practised during the year.
- Identify areas where you feel you can still improve.
- Make a list of people or material that can help you and make a plan of action for the holidays or the next year.

Macmillan Education
4 Crinan Street
London N1 9XW
A division of Springer Nature Limited

Companies and representatives throughout the world

ISBN 978-0-230-47100-9

Written by Lynda Edwards and Patricia Reilly

This edition published 2016
First edition entitled "Gateway B2+ Workbook" published 2011

Designed by emc design ltd
Illustrated by Laura Martinez (Sylvie Poggio Artists) p10
Cover design by emc design ltd and Springer Nature Ltd
Cover/photograph by Getty images/Dougal Waters, Thinkstock/Zoonar/N.Okhitin
Picture research by Emily Taylor

The publishers would like to thank staff and pupils at the following schools in Mexico and Spain for helping us so enthusiastically with our research for the course:
Concha Campos, IES Burgo de Las Rozas, Las Rozas, Madrid; Félix Gaspar, IES Las Encinas; Villanueva de la Cañada, Madrid; Cristina Moisen, IES Joaquín Turina, Madrid; Colegio Montessori Cuautitlán; Colegio Conrad Gessner; Colegio Erasmo de Rotterdam; Colegio Kanic, Centro Educativo Erich Fromm; Universidad Franco Mexicana; Centro Pedagógico María Montessori de Ecatepec; Instituto Cultural; Escuela Maestro Manuel Acosta; Liceo Sakbé De México.

The publishers would also like to thank all those who reviewed or piloted the first edition of Gateway:
Benjamin Affolter, Evelyn Andorfer, Anna Ciereszynska, Regina Culver, Anna Dabrowska, Justyna Deja, Ondrej Dosedel, Lisa Durham, Dagmar Eder, Eva Ellederovan, H Fouad, Sabrina Funes, Luiza Gervescu, Isabel González Bueno, Jutta Habringer, Stela Halmageanu, Marta Hilgier, Andrea Hutterer, Nicole Ioakimidis, Mag. Annemarie Kammerhofer, Irina Kondrasheva, Sonja Lengauer, Gabriela Liptakova, Andrea Littlewood, María Cristina Maggi, Silvia Miranda Barbara Nowak, Agnieska Orlińska, Anna Orlowska, María Paula Palou, Marta Piotrowska, N Reda, Katharina Schatz, Roswitha Schwarz, Barbara Ścibor, Katarzyna Sochacka, Joanna Spoz, Monica Srtygner, Marisol Suppan, Stephanie Sutter, Halina Tyliba, Prilipko, Maria Vizgina, Vladyko, Pia Wimmer, Katarzyna Zadrożna-Attia and Katarzyna Zaremba-Jaworska.

The authors and publishers would like to thank the following for permission to reproduce their photographs:
Alamy/Arterra Picture Library p88, Alamy/Aurora Photos p71(br), Alamy/J.R.Bale p82, Alamy/Blend Images p64(br), Alamy/Cate Brown p71(Bl), Alamy/Adam Burton p54(A), Alamy/Gareth Byrne p63(B), Alamy/J C Clamp p74, Alamy/Cultura Creative pp38, Alamy/Glow Asia RF p85(B), Alamy/Ikon Images p23(bl), Alamy/Image Source p71(Ar), Alamy/Juice Images p25(yoga), Alamy/Norma Jean Gargasz p53(B), Alamy/LH Images p86, Alamy/Gilles Larbi p49(tl), Alamy/MBI pp14, 63(D), 81(D), Alamy/MIKA – Images p63(C), Alamy/Justin Minns p56, Alamy/OJO Images Ltd pp31(cr), 77(tr), Alamy/Mark Phillips p71(Cr), Alamy/Jordi De Rueda Roigé p41(br), Alamy/SERDAR p12(b), Alamy/Dmitriy Shironosov p7, Alamy/Radius Images p25(food), Alamy/Space Images p25(violin), Alamy/Steve Vidlerb p5(br), Alamy/Hongqi Zhang p89(br); **BANANASTOCK** p20(C); **Corbis** p68, Corbis/Ashley Cooper p71(Cl), Corbis/Jim Craigmyle p41(tl), Corbis/Dave and Les Jacobs/Blend Images p77(b), Corbis/J.James p44; **Getty** pp5(tr), 36, 45, Getty/artpartner-images p59(tl), Getty/Tony Anderson p25(dance), Getty/Barcroft p67(t,br), Getty/Thomas Barwick p64(cl), Getty/Oliver Burston p23(tr,bl), Getty Images/Cartesia p13(tr), Getty/Doug Cheeseman p17(B), Getty/MIKE CLARKE p5(cl), Getty/DRB Images, LLC p85(A), Getty/Robert Daly p80, Getty/Nick David p53(A), Getty/John Fedele p92, Getty/Michael & Patricia Fogden p34, Getty/Benjamin Van De Grift /EyeEm p54(tr), Getty/Melanie Dawn Harte p41(tr), Getty/Hero Images p89(tl), Getty/Image Source p17(A), Getty/Dave and Les Jacobs p43, Getty/Jupiterimages p62, Getty/Photography by Steve Kelley aka mudpig p59(bl), Getty/ Kevin Landwer-Johan p17(D), Getty/WADE LAUBE/Fairfax Media p5(tl), Getty/Romilly Lockye p63(A), Getty/Jason Moskowitz p71(Al), Getty/Bryan Mullennix p59(t), Getty/PeopleImages.com p81(C), Getty/Monty Rakusen p81(B), Getty/David Schaffer p78, Getty/Science Photo Library – PASIEKA p31(tr, insert), Getty/Will Salter p17(C), Getty/Witold Skrypczak p18, Getty/Burcin Tuncer p27, Getty/ullstein bild p51, Getty/VWB photos p54(B), Getty/Westend61 p9, Getty/Granger Wootz p5(cr); **ImageSource** pp20(A), 81(E), Image Source/Charles Gullung CM p20(B); **Macmillan Publishers Ltd**/Rob Judges p63(E); **PhotoDisc**/Getty Images p85(tl); **Rex**/Action Press p26, Rex/Chris Cooper p49(cl), Rex/Snap Stills p28, Rex/Jochen Tack p49(bl), Rex/TinyHouseBuild p49(tl); **Thinkstock Images**/AVAVA p81(A), Thinkstock Images/Dmitrijs Dmitrijevs p60, Thinkstock Images/moodboard p85(br), Thinkstock/Vitaliy Pakhnyushchyy p31(mouse), Thinkstock/maki sasaki p21.

The authors and publishers are grateful for permission to reprint the following copyright material:
Adapted material from 'Vedika Dalmia: 'Where Should I Start?' – Carving a Career in Tech'; 'Anna Shaw: Inspiring the next generation of female scientists' and 'Star-gazing from South Wales'. © 2015 WISE Campaign. Originally published on www.wisecampaign.org.uk. Reprinted with permission.
Extract from 'From petty crime to small business in one smart move' by Mary O'Hara. © 2008 Guardian News and Media Limited. Originally published at www.theguardian.com. Reprinted with permission.
Extract from 'Man on wire' by Mark Zakian. © 2010 Guardian News and Media Limited. Originally published at www.theguardian.com. Reprinted with permission.
Extract from 'Experience: I fell 6,000 feet and survived' by James Boole. © 2009 Guardian News and Media Limited. Originally published at www.theguardian.com. Reprinted with permission.

Printed and bound in Lebanon
2021 2020 2019 2018
10 9 8 7 6